Five Plays From
SHAKESPEARE

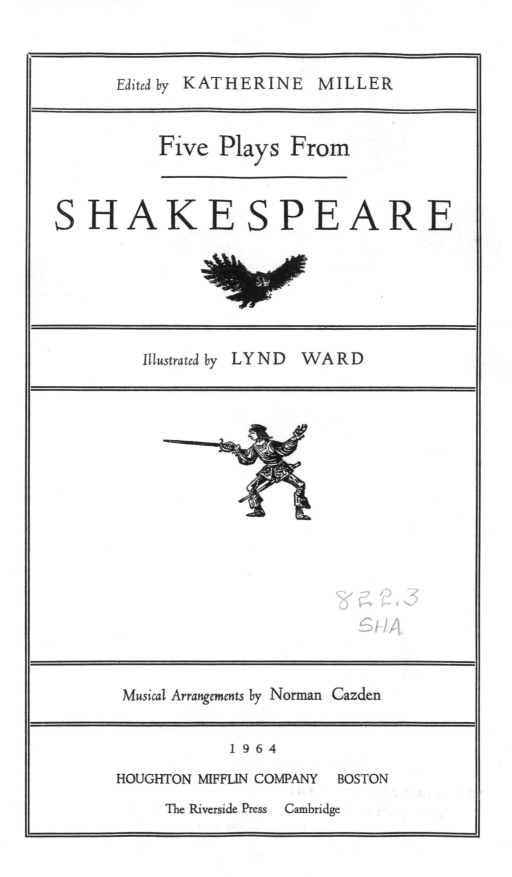

Edited by KATHERINE MILLER

Five Plays From

SHAKESPEARE

Illustrated by LYND WARD

Musical Arrangements by Norman Cazden

1 9 6 4

HOUGHTON MIFFLIN COMPANY   BOSTON

The Riverside Press   Cambridge

For Nancy and Don

ACKNOWLEDGMENTS

I AM deeply indebted to the scholars whose work I have used as my principal guides in preparing this volume. (I have deviated from them and must bear the blame for errors and distortions.) For "The Tempest," "Macbeth," and "Julius Caesar," *The Yale Shakespeare,* Revised Edition (New Haven: Yale University Press, published 1955, 1954, and 1959 respectively); for "A Midsummer Night's Dream," the *Laurel Shakespeare* (New York: Dell Publishing Company, 1960); and for "The Comedy of Errors," *The New Shakespeare,* Second Edition (New York: Cambridge University Press, 1962).

CONTENTS

To the Reader

FOR THE most absurd and glorious nonsense, no one can compare with Shakespeare. For monstrous murders and brooding horror, for scenes to touch your heart, or break it, for the most blithely starry-eyed lovers, and for the most magnificent music ever made with words, you will never find anyone better. When you meet him for the first time, however, you must dig for the treasure; I have tried in this book to make the digging easier.

In the first place, the very fact that these are plays rather than stories creates some difficulty, because plays tell only what people say. Everything they do or think or feel you must imagine for yourself. Therefore, I have inserted explanations here and there about what is going on. In the second place, Shakespeare took his plots two and three at a time and wove them together in delightful but difficult patterns. So I have added occasional comments designed to help readers follow the thread of the story.

It is with the language, however, that you may experience your greatest difficulty — and greatest pleasure. Since the plays were written there have been many changes in the English language: new words have been added, old ones have fallen into disuse or come to be used differently, and styles in the shaping of sentences have changed. In order to understand him, therefore, it is necessary to put yourself to a little trouble — but, fortunately, only a little. For the truly remarkable thing is how clearly Shakespeare speaks to us from the distance of almost four hundred years.

The five plays included here have been shortened to bring quicker understanding and enjoyment. Each play is about half its original length. Long conversations and complicating subplots have been cut in order to concentrate the action and keep the story moving swiftly. My major concern in deciding what to leave out has been to tell the story clearly, followed closely by the desire to do as little injury as possible to the rhythm of the poetry. About ninety per cent of the lines here are just as Shakespeare wrote them. Sometimes, however, the last half of one line has been spliced to the first half of another, and occasionally I have regrouped words and phrases, thus producing lines not composed by Shakespeare. The scholarly thing to do would be to enclose these lines in square brackets. But it has been my experience that brackets can distort the meaning for some readers, causing them to treat the bracketed words as if they were in parentheses. In this volume, therefore, there are no brackets. The plays are to be enjoyed; time enough later for scholarly details.

In reading, try first for a grasp of a play as a whole, or for the sense of a whole scene, at least. Read a play (or a scene) all the way through, then go back and read it again, referring to the Glossary for help with unfamiliar words. Sometimes even a familiar word will not make proper sense (a *bottle* of hay, for example); in such a case remember that words may be used differently at different times, and consult the Glossary.

Simply by reading this book to yourself, you can get great enjoyment from the plot and a real feel for the music of Shakespeare's language. But no matter how completely the play comes to life in your imagination, it can never quite take the place of an actual performance. These plays were born on the stage, in the hurly-burly of an active theater, and that is where they come alive. Each play can be performed in an hour, a length that has proved to be a good one for young people, performers and audiences as well. Turn to the back of the book for suggestions to help you plan a production and for complete musical settings for each of the plays. Except for the melodies of a very few songs, the music that accompanied the plays originally has been lost. If Shakespeare followed the usual practice of his day, however, he borrowed freely from music then popular in London. Norman Cazden — musicologist, composer, and teacher — has done the same.

Now on to the plays. Read them, perform them — enjoy them. "My project . . . was to please," said Shakespeare; and so he does.

KM

A Short Chronology

(dates for plays are approximate)

1558	Elizabeth I became Queen of England
1564 (April)	William Shakespeare was born
1588	The Spanish Armada was defeated
1591 or 1592	*The Comedy of Errors* was written
1595 or 1596	*A Midsummer Night's Dream* was written
1599	*Julius Caesar* was written
1603	James I became King of England
1606	*Macbeth* was written
1607	Jamestown, Virginia, was settled
1610 or 1611	*The Tempest* was written
1616 (April)	Shakespeare died
1623	Shakespeare's friends published his collected plays (the First Folio)

1

The Tempest

Faraway Places

1

FOR CENTURIES men living in the lands around the Mediterranean sailed their tiny ships from side to side and from end to end of that sea — the sea they named the "Middle-of-the-World Sea." To these early sailors a voyage from one end of the Mediterranean to the other was literally a voyage to the end of the earth. Later, as seamen dared to go beyond the Pillars of Hercules into the Atlantic and up around the western shores of Europe, civilization spread. Before many centuries had passed, sailors from Spain and Portugal, from Scandinavia, Britain, Holland, and France, were sailing to and from ports all up and down the western side of Europe. The Mediterranean was no longer the center of the world.

In the fifteenth century men ventured farther and explored the whole length of the Atlantic coast of Africa. Some were even bold enough to make the dangerous voyage around its southern tip to the Far East, with its wealth of silks, spices, and exotic perfumes. And finally, in 1492, Christopher Columbus dared to search for the East by sailing west — into the unknown.

The ordinary man of the sixteenth century had only vague ideas about geography. Maps were few and far from accurate. By the end of the century most people living around seaports probably knew that the world was round, for Magellan's expedition had circled the globe in 1519–22. Nevertheless, there was still much confusion in men's minds about what lands lay across the Atlantic. Columbus had called the natives there Indians, because he believed that he had reached India, and it is likely that many people did not yet know that a huge new world lay between Europe and Asia.

In the taverns and inns of London sailors back from voyages to distant places told of strange and fearful things they had seen — of savage storms in wild uncharted waters, of pygmies black as night, of feathered and painted Indians in lands far to the west. Their imaginations conjured up unbelievable wonders out of things like hippopotamuses, cotton plants, and sea lions, for they came back from their journeys bearing tales of monstrous four-legged fish with heads like oxen and hard wart-covered shells, of sheep trees that bore whole sheep instead of fruit, and of sea sirens who lifted their bodies above the surface of the sea. They told

... of antres vast and deserts idle,
Rough quarries, rocks, and hills whose heads touch heaven,
And of the Cannibals that each other eat,
The Anthropophagi, and men whose heads
Do grow beneath their shoulders.

In this sixteenth-century world people believed almost any kind of creature was possible. No one knew which of the strange new beings were men and which were animals. Were pygmies men? Were chimpanzees? Were Indians? At first people called orangutangs "wild men of the woods." They even thought some of the things they saw were creatures of the devil. For people of the sixteenth century believed firmly in ghosts and demons, in fairies, elves, and sprites. Even a century later, in 1692, men and women in Salem, Massachusetts, would be hanged for being witches.

In 1607 the first permanent English settlement was made in the New World at Jamestown (named for King James) in Virginia (named for their former ruler, Elizabeth, the Virgin Queen). In June of 1609 a fleet of ships bringing reinforcements, fresh supplies, and a governor for the new province, set sail from Plymouth, England. A terrible storm scattered the fleet. Although most of the ships finally reached Jamestown in August, the flagship of the fleet, the *Sea Adventure*, was missing. It had been blown far off its course and wrecked on Bermuda, an island with the fearful reputation of being inhabited by demons. There the voyagers remained for nine months until they had managed to build two small boats in which they arrived in Jamestown in May of 1610.

Later, members of the party wrote accounts of their adventures on the "Ile of Divels," as Bermuda was called. One of them, named R. Rich, wrote a ballad about their adventures. A ballad was a very common way of spreading news in those days when there were no newspapers. Copies of the ballad were sold in London, and minstrels sang it in the villages and towns. Rich's ballad was published under the headline "News from Virginia" and was entitled "The Lost Flock Triumphant." On the title page was this explanatory phrase, "With the manner of their distress in the Iland of Devils (otherwise called Bermoothawes)."

Another member of the company, William Strachy, described their terrifying experience in these words:

A dreadful storm and hideous at length did beat all light from heaven; which like an hell of darkness turned black upon us. Fury added to fury. Our clamors drowned in the winds, and the winds in thunder. The sea swelled above the clouds, and gave battle unto heaven. It could not be said to rain, the waters like whole rivers did flood in the air. An apparition of a little round light, like a faint star, trembling, and streaming along with a sparkling blaze, half the height upon the main mast, and shooting sometimes from shroud to shroud, half the night kept with us.

Sir George Summers, when no man dreamed of such happiness discovered and cried Land. We found it to be the dangerous and dreaded Ilands of the

2

Bermuda. They be so terrible to all that ever touched on them, and such tempests, thunders, and other fearful objects are seen and heard about them, that they be called commonly, the Devils Ilands, and are feared and avoided of all sea travelers alive, above any other place in the world, it being counted of most, that they can be no habitation for men, but rather given over to devils and wicked spirits.

At the time these things were taking place there was in London a poet, who was also an actor and playwright. He was probably thinking of these Ilands of Devils when he devised a setting for one of his plays. He was certainly thinking of all the tales of shipwreck and storm he had heard sailors tell in the taverns of London when he wrote of a ship wrecked in a tempest on an unknown island. His idea of the geography of the world he lived in was just as confused as anyone's. To him Egypt, Tunis, Italy — and Virginia — were all equally faraway places, for he wrecked his ship at Bermuda when it was on a voyage from North Africa to Italy. And he seems to have believed, as did the average man of his day, in magic, for he filled his play with enchantments.

The Tempest

1

The Characters:

ALONSO, King of Naples
SEBASTIAN, his brother
PROSPERO, the right Duke of Milan
ANTONIO, his brother, the usurping Duke of Milan
FERDINAND, son to the King of Naples
GONZALO, an honest old councilor
ADRIAN, a lord
FRANCISCO, another lord
CALIBAN, a savage and deformed slave
TRINCULO, a jester
STEPHANO, a drunken butler
MASTER OF A SHIP
BOATSWAIN
MARINERS
MIRANDA, daughter to Prospero
ARIEL, an airy spirit
SPIRITS

The Scene: An uninhabited island

This is one of the last plays that Shakespeare ever wrote. In it he transports his audience to an enchanted island far, far away. The island is inhabited solely by spirits, except for a sorcerer, his lovely daughter, and a creature that is part man, part beast, and part demon. The first scene in the play is a violent storm that the sorcerer has conjured up by his magic. Imagine him,

4

standing high on a rocky promontory, his magic wand in his outstretched hand, his mantle whipped by the wind. He is watching a ship tossed in the storm and listening to the shouts and cries of the terrified men on board.

Prologue

A tempestuous noise of thunder and lightning.
Enter a Shipmaster and a Boatswain.

MASTER	Boatswain!
BOATSWAIN	Here, Master! What cheer?
MASTER	Speak to th' mariners. Fall to 't, yarely, or we run ourselves aground — bestir, bestir! *Exit.*

Enter Mariners.

BOATSWAIN	Heigh, my hearts! Cheerly, cheerly, my hearts! Yare, yare! Take in the topsail! *Exeunt Mariners.*

Enter Alonso, Sebastian, Antonio, Ferdinand, Gonzalo, and others.

ALONSO	Good Boatswain, have care! Where's the Master?
BOATSWAIN	I pray now, keep below.
ANTONIO	Where is the Master, Bosun?
BOATSWAIN	Do you not hear him? You mar our labor. Keep your cabins!
GONZALO	Nay, good, be patient.
BOATSWAIN	When the sea is. Hence! What care these roarers for the name of King? To cabin: trouble us not!
GONZALO	Good, yet remember whom thou hast aboard.
BOATSWAIN	None that I more love than myself. Out of our way,.I say. *Exit.*
GONZALO	I have great comfort from this fellow: methinks he hath no drowning mark upon him. If he be not born to be hanged, our case is miserable. *Exeunt Alonso and Ferdinand.*

Enter Boatswain.

BOATSWAIN	Down with the topmast! Yare, lower, lower!

Enter Mariners, wet.

MARINERS	All lost! To prayers, to prayers, all lost! *Exeunt Mariners and Boatswain.*
VOICES	*Within.* Mercy on us! We split, we split! Farewell, brother! We split, we split, we split!
ANTONIO	Let's all sink wi' th' King.
SEBASTIAN	Let's take leave of him. *Exeunt Sebastian and Antonio.*
GONZALO	Now would I give a thousand furlongs of sea for an acre of barren ground: long heath, brown furze, anything. The wills above be done, but I would fain die a dry death. *Exeunt.*

5

ACT I

Scene 1

Miranda watches, too, as the ship is dashed to pieces on the rocks. When she begs her father to still the waters, he assures her no one has been harmed. Then, after removing his magic mantle, he tells her a story. Twelve years ago he, Prospero, was the Duke of Milan (a fairytale country bearing little resemblance to the historical Duchy of Milan in northern Italy). But he was not a good ruler, for he gave no thought to the welfare of his people. Instead he spent all his time in secret studies and left the government in the hands of his brother Antonio. And Antonio was evil. He plotted with the King of Naples to usurp the dukedom from Prospero, promising that if the King would help to overthrow Prospero and make him, Antonio, the Duke, he would pay yearly tribute (or taxes) to Naples. This the King agreed to. Consequently, Prospero and little Miranda were kidnaped, taken far out to sea, and there set adrift to die in a derelict ship. One person, Gonzalo, was loyal to Prospero. He provided the ship with food, water, clothing, and — most important — Prospero's books on magic. Fortune, too, was kind and they drifted safely to this beautiful island. Now Fortune has smiled once more and brought to the island the very men who had wronged Prospero. That is the reason for the storm.

The instrument through whom Prospero raised the storm — and saved the ship and the voyagers — is the airy spirit Ariel. When Prospero first came to the island he found Ariel caught in the trunk of a tree, where he had been imprisoned by a foul witch named Sycorax. By his magic art Prospero released Ariel from his torture. Since then Ariel has shown his gratitude by obeying Prospero's commands.

Enter Prospero and Miranda.

MIRANDA   If by your art, my dearest father, you have
Put the wild waters in this roar, allay them.
O! I have suffer'd with those that I saw suffer:
A vessel — who had some noble creatures in her —
Dash'd all to pieces. O poor souls, they perish'd.

PROSPERO   There's no harm done.

MIRANDA   O woe the day!

PROSPERO   No harm.

I have done nothing but in care of thee —
Of thee my dear one, thee my daughter — who
Art ignorant of what thou art. 'Tis time
I should inform thee farther: Lend thy hand
And pluck my magic garment from me. *Lays down mantle.* So,
Lie there, my art. Wipe thou thine eyes; have comfort;
The direful spectacle of the wreck which touch'd
The very virtue of compassion in thee
I have so safely order'd that there is
Not so much perdition as an hair
Betid to any creature in the vessel
Which thou heard'st cry, which thou saw'st sink. Sit down,
Obey and be attentive. Canst thou remember
A time before we came unto this cell?
I do not think thou canst, for then thou wast not
Out three years old.

MIRANDA   Certainly, sir. 'Tis far off,
And rather like a dream than an assurance
That my remembrance warrants. Had I not
Four or five women once that tended me?

PROSPERO   Thou hadst, and more, Miranda. Twelve year since,
Thy father was the Duke of Milan and
A prince of power.

MIRANDA   Sir, are not you my father?

PROSPERO   'Tis sure thou art my daughter — and thy father
Was Duke of Milan — and his only heir
A princess.

MIRANDA   O! the heavens.

PROSPERO   I pray thee mark me.
Neglecting worldly ends, all dedicated
To closeness and the bettering of my mind,
The government I cast upon my brother,
And to my state grew stranger, being transported
And rapt in secret studies; thy false uncle —
My brother and thy uncle, call'd Antonio —
Whom next thyself of all the world I lov'd,
Didst then confederate with th' King of Naples.
Dost thou hear?

MIRANDA   Your tale, sir, would cure deafness.

PROSPERO   This King of Naples hearkens my brother's suit,
Which was that he in lieu o' th' premises
Of homage and I know not how much tribute
Should presently extirpate me and mine
Out of the dukedom and confer fair Milan,

	With all the honors, on my brother; whereon,
	A treacherous army levied, one midnight
	Fated to th' purpose did Antonio open
	The gates of Milan, and i' th' dead of darkness
	The ministers for th' purpose hurried thence
	Me and thy crying self, and aboard a bark
	Bore us some leagues to sea, where they prepar'd
	A rotten carcass of a boat; the rats
	Instinctively have quit it. There they hoist us,
	To cry to th' sea that roar'd to us, to sigh
	To th' winds whose pity, sighing back again,
	Did us but loving wrong.

MIRANDA   How came we ashore?

PROSPERO   By Providence divine.
Some food we had, and some fresh water, that
A noble Neopolitan, Gonzalo,
Out of his charity did give us, with
Rich garments, linens, stuffs, and necessaries
Which since have steaded much; so of his gentleness,
Knowing I lov'd my books, he furnish'd me
From my own library with volumes that
I prize above my dukedom. Now I arise. *Resumes his mantle.*
Sit still and hear the last of our sea-sorrow.
Here in this island we arriv'd, and here
Have I thy schoolmaster and thy tutor been.

MIRANDA   Heavens thank you for 't! And now I pray your reason
For raising this sea storm?

PROSPERO   Bountiful fortune —
Now my dear lady — hath mine enemies
Brought to this shore. Here cease more questions.
Thou art inclin'd to sleep; 'tis a good dullness,
And give it way — I know thou canst not choose.
Miranda sleeps.
Come away, Ariel, come! I am ready now.
Enter Ariel.

ARIEL   All hail, great master, grave sir, hail! I come
To answer thy best pleasure, be 't to fly,
To swim, to dive into the fire, to ride
On the curled clouds.

PROSPERO   Hast thou, spirit,
Perform'd to point the tempest that I bade thee?

ARIEL   To every article.
I boarded the King's ship; now in the beak,
Now in the waist, the deck, in every cabin

I flam'd amazement; sometimes I'd divide
And burn in many places; on the topmast,
The yards and bowsprit would I flame distinctly,
And then meet and join. The fire and cracks
Of sulphurous roaring the most mighty Neptune
Seem to besiege, and make his bold waves tremble,
Yea, his dread trident shake. All but mariners
Plung'd in the foaming brine and quit the vessel,
Then all afire with me; the King's son Ferdinand,
With hair up-staring — then like reeds, not hair —
Was the first man that leapt, cried "Hell is empty,
And all the devils are here!"

PROSPERO   Why, that's my spirit!
But are they, Ariel, safe?

ARIEL   Not a hair perish'd:
On their sustaining garments not a blemish,
But fresher than before; and as thou bad'st me,
In troops I have dispers'd them 'bout the isle.
The King's son have I landed by himself.
The ship is hid in the deep nook where once
Thou call'dst me up at midnight to fetch dew
From the still-vex'd Bermoothes.

PROSPERO   Ariel, thy charge
Exactly is perform'd; but there's more work.
What is the time o' th' day?

ARIEL   Past the mid season.

PROSPERO   At least two glasses. The time 'twixt six and now
Must by us both be spent most preciously.

ARIEL   Is there more toil? Since thou dost give me pains,
Let me remember thee what thou hast promis'd.

PROSPERO   What is 't thou canst demand?

ARIEL   My liberty.

PROSPERO   Before the time be out? No more!

ARIEL   I prithee
Remember I have done thee worthy service
Without or grudge or grumblings; thou didst promise
To bate me a full year.

PROSPERO   Dost thou forget
From what a torment I did free thee?

ARIEL   No.

PROSPERO   Hast thou forgot the foul witch Sycorax?
As thou report'st thyself, thou wast her servant,
And, for thou wast a spirit too delicate
To act her abhorr'd commands, she did confine thee
Into a cloven pine, within which rift

	Imprison'd thou didst painfully remain
	A dozen years; within which space she died
	And left thee there. Then was this island —
	Save for the son that she did litter here —
	A freckled whelp, hag-born — not honor'd with
	A human shape.

ARIEL   Yes, Caliban her son.

PROSPERO Whom now I keep in service. Thou best know'st
What torment I did find thee in; thy groans
Did make wolves howl, and penetrate the breasts
Of ever-angry bears; it was mine art,
When I arriv'd and heard thee, that made gape
The pine and let thee out.

ARIEL   I thank thee, master.
I will be correspondent to command
And do my spriting, gently.

PROSPERO Do so, and after two days I will discharge thee.

ARIEL That's my noble master!
What shall I do? Say what! What shall I do?

PROSPERO Go make thyself like a nymph o' th' sea; be subject
To no sight but thine and mine, invisible
To every eyeball else.

ARIEL   It shall be done.   *Exit.*

*Aside from the spirits, the only creature on the island when
Prospero arrived was a poor misshapen monster named Caliban,
the son of the witch Sycorax. (No one knows why Shakespeare
named him Caliban, but it is a curious coincidence, if it is a
coincidence, that by the simple exchange of the sounds l and n,
"Caliban" becomes "cannibal.") Prospero was kind to Caliban;
he fed him, petted him, and even taught him to talk, until Caliban tried to harm Miranda. Then Prospero recognized him for
the demon he was and forced him to become his slave.*

PROSPERO Awake, dear heart, awake; thou hast slept well;
Awake.

MIRANDA   The strangeness of your story put
Heaviness in me.

PROSPERO   Shake it off! Come on,
We'll visit Caliban.

MIRANDA   'Tis a villain, sir,
I do not love to look on.

PROSPERO He does make our fire,
Fetch in our wood, and serves in offices
That profit us. What ho, slave! Caliban!

	Thou earth, thou! Speak!
CALIBAN	*Within.* There's wood enough within.
PROSPERO	Thou poisonous slave, got by the devil himself
	Upon thy wicked dam, come forth.
	Enter Caliban.
CALIBAN	As wicked dew as e'er my mother brush'd
	With raven's feather from unwholesome fen
	Drop on you both!
PROSPERO	For this be sure tonight thou shalt have cramps.
CALIBAN	This island's mine by Sycorax my mother,
	Which thou tak'st from me! When thou camest first,
	Thou strok'st me and made much of me; wouldst give me
	Water with berries in 't, and teach me how
	To name the bigger light and how the less,
	That burn by day and night; and then I lov'd thee
	And show'd thee all the qualities o' th' isle,
	The fresh springs, brine pits, barren place and fertile.
	Curs'd be I that did so!
PROSPERO	I have used thee —
	Filth as thou art — with human care and lodg'd thee
	In mine own cell, till thou didst seek to violate
	The honor of my child, abhorred slave.
CALIBAN	You taught me language and my profit on 't
	Is, I know how to curse!

PROSPERO	Hag-seed, hence!

Fetch us in fuel, and be quick thou 'rt best.
If you neglect'st, or dost unwillingly
What I command, I'll rack thee with old cramps,
Fill all thy bones with aches, make thee roar
That beasts shall tremble at thy din.

CALIBAN   No, pray thee!
I must obey; his art is of such power.

PROSPERO   So, slave, hence!   *Exit Caliban.*

Everything that happens in this play, including the storm, is under Prospero's magic control. The invisible Ariel now leads in one of the passengers from the ill-fated vessel. This is Ferdinand, the son of the King of Naples. Prospero allows Ferdinand and Miranda to see each other knowing well what will happen. When it does, Prospero's behavior suddenly changes. He pretends great harshness and accuses Ferdinand of being a spy. In response to the accusation Ferdinand draws his sword, but Prospero casts a magic spell on him and takes him prisoner. All this, as will be seen, is to test Ferdinand's love for Miranda.

Enter Ferdinand; and Ariel, invisible, singing.

ARIEL   Come unto these yellow sands,
                  and then take hands:
              Curtsied when you have, and kiss'd,
                  the wild waves whist,
              Foot it featly here and there,
              And sweet sprites the burthen bear.

VOICES   *Singing the burthen, dispersedly.*
              Hark, hark! Bow wow!
              The watch-dogs bark! Bow wow!

ARIEL   Hark, hark! I hear
                  The strain of strutting Chanticleer
              Cry cockadiddle-dow!

FERDINAND   Where should this music be? I' th' air, or th' earth?
              It sounds no more! And sure it waits upon
              Some god o' th' island; sitting on a bank,
              Weeping again the King my father's wrack,
              This music crept by me upon the waters,
              Allaying both their fury and my passion.

ARIEL   Full fathom five thy father lies;
              Of his bones are coral made;
              Those are pearls that were his eyes:
              Nothing of him that doth fade,
              But doth suffer a sea change

13

	Into something rich and strange.
	Sea nymphs hourly ring his knell.
VOICES	Ding dong!
ARIEL	Hark, now I hear them! Ding-dong bell.
FERDINAND	The ditty does remember my drown'd father.
PROSPERO	The fringed curtains of thine eye advance
	And say what thou seest yond.
MIRANDA	What is 't? a spirit?
PROSPERO	No, wench, it eats and sleeps and hath such senses
	As we have, such. This gallant which thou seest
	Was in the wreck. He hath lost his fellows
	And strays about to find 'em.
MIRANDA	I might call him
	A thing divine, for nothing natural
	I ever saw so noble.
FERDINAND	Most sure the goddess
	On whom these airs attend! O you wonder!
	Be you a maid or no?
MIRANDA	No wonder, sir,
	But certainly a maid.
FERDINAND	My language? Heavens!
	I am the best of them that speak this speech
	Were I but where 'tis spoken.
PROSPERO	How? The best?
	What wert thou if the King of Naples heard thee?
FERDINAND	A single thing, as I am now, that wonders
	To hear thee speak of Naples! Myself am Naples,
	Who with mine eyes — never since at ebb — beheld
	The King my father wreck'd.
PROSPERO	*Aside.* At the first sight
	They have chang'd eyes! Delicate Ariel,
	I'll set thee free for this. — A word, good sir.
MIRANDA	Why speaks my father so ungently? This
	Is the third man that e'er I saw! The first
	That e'er I sigh'd for! Pity move my father
	To be inclin'd my way.
FERDINAND	O, if a virgin,
	And your affection not gone forth, I'll make you
	The Queen of Naples.
PROSPERO	Soft, sir. One word more.
	Aside. They are both in either's powers! But this swift business
	I must uneasy make, lest too light winning
	Make the prize light. — One word more! I charge thee
	That thou attend me! Thou dost here usurp
	The name thou ow'st not and hast put thyself

14

	Upon this island as a spy, to win it
	From me, the lord on 't.
FERDINAND	No, as I am a man.
MIRANDA	There's nothing ill can dwell in such a temple.
PROSPERO	Speak not you for him! He's a traitor! Come,
	I'll manacle thy neck and feet together!
FERDINAND	I will resist such entertainment till
	Mine enemy has more power.
	He draws, and is charmed from moving.
MIRANDA	O dear Father,
	Make not too rash a trial of him, for
	He's gentle and not fearful.
PROSPERO	Put thy sword up.
	Thou mak'st a show, but dar'st not strike, thy conscience
	Is so possess'd with guilt!
MIRANDA	Beseech you, Father!

PROSPERO	Hence! Hang not on my garments.
MIRANDA	Sir, have pity!
PROSPERO	Thou think'st there is no more such shapes as he,
	Having seen but him and Caliban! Foolish wench,
	To th' most of men this is a Caliban,
	And they to him are angels.
MIRANDA	My affections
	Are then most humble: I have no ambition
	To see a goodlier man.
PROSPERO	*To Ferdinand.* Come on, obey!
FERDINAND	My spirits, as in a dream, are all bound up.
PROSPERO	Thou hast done well, fine Ariel!
MIRANDA	Be of comfort.
	My father's of a better nature, sir,
	Than he appears by speech: this is unwonted
	Which now came from him.
PROSPERO	*To Ariel.* Thou shalt be as free
	As mountain winds; but then exactly do
	All points of my command.
ARIEL	To th' syllable.
PROSPERO	*To Ferdinand.* Come, follow! *To Miranda.* Speak not for him.
	Exeunt.

Scene 2

Prospero's plan is to make his brother Antonio (the usurping Duke of Milan) and Alonso (the King of Naples) suffer for the wrongs they did him, and then to force them to give him back his dukedom. The tempest, and the fear they felt then, was their first punishment. Now, miraculously brought safely to shore, this little group thinks they are the only survivors. For Alonso that means the loss of his son, and in his grief he is inconsolable. Among the lords trying to comfort him is Gonzalo, the kind old man who had helped save Prospero and Miranda from death.

Soon Ariel appears and mercifully charms them to sleep — all, that is, except Antonio and the King's brother Sebastian. Antonio takes this opportunity to tempt Sebastian to seize his brother's crown. How easy it would be, he says, with both of Alonso's heirs now out of the way, his son drowned and his daughter married and living in Africa. Antonio even offers to help Sebastian: Antonio will kill Alonso for him if at the same

moment Sebastian will kill Gonzalo, whose noble nature An-
tonio does not trust. In payment for Antonio's assistance Milan
will be freed from the obligation of paying tribute to Naples —
that is what Antonio is really after!

Enter Alonso, Sebastian, Antonio, Gonzalo, Adrian, Francisco,
and others.

GONZALO   Beseech you, sir, be merry; you have cause —
             So have we all — of joy, for our escape
             Is much beyond our loss.

ALONSO   Prithee, peace.

SEBASTIAN   He receives comfort like cold porridge.

GONZALO   Here is everything advantageous to life.

ANTONIO   True, save means to live.

SEBASTIAN   Of that there's none, or little.

ADRIAN   How lush and lusty the grass looks! How green!

GONZALO   But the rarity of it is — which is indeed almost beyond credit
             — that our garments being — as they were — drench'd in the
             sea, are now as fresh as when we put them on first in Afric, at
             the marriage of the King's fair daughter Claribel to the King of
             Tunis.

SEBASTIAN   'Twas a sweet marriage, and we prosper well in our return.

ALONSO   You cram these words into mine ears against
             The stomach of my sense. Would I had never
             Married my daughter there, for coming thence
             My only son is lost.

FRANCISCO   Sir, he may live.
             I saw him beat the surges under him
             And ride upon their backs. I do not doubt
             He came alive to land.

ALONSO   No, no, he's gone.

             Enter Ariel playing solemn music.

ADRIAN   The air breathes upon us here most sweetly.

GONZALO   I must sleep, for I am very heavy.

             All sleep but Alonso, Sebastian, and Antonio.

ALONSO   What, all so soon asleep? I wish mine eyes
             Would, with themselves, shut up my thoughts. I find
             They are inclin'd to do so.

SEBASTIAN   Please you, sir.
             Do not omit the heavy offer of it.
             It seldom visits sorrow; when it doth
             It is a comforter.

ANTONIO   We two, my lord,
             Will guard your person while you take your rest,
             And watch your safety.

ALONSO	Thank you. Wondrous heavy . . .
	Alonso sleeps. Exit Ariel.
SEBASTIAN	What a strange drowsiness possesses them!
ANTONIO	It is the quality o' th' climate.
SEBASTIAN	Why
	Doth it not then our eyelids sink? I find not
	Myself dispos'd to sleep.
ANTONIO	Nor I: my spirits are nimble.
	They fell together all as by consent;
	They dropp'd as by a thunderstroke. What might,
	Worthy Sebastian? O what might —? No more!
	And yet, my imagination sees a crown
	Dropping upon thy head.
SEBASTIAN	What? Art thou waking?
ANTONIO	Do you not hear me speak?
SEBASTIAN	I do, and surely
	It is a sleepy language, and thou speak'st
	Out of thy sleep! What is it thou didst say,
	And yet so fast asleep?
ANTONIO	Noble Sebastian, thou let'st thy fortune sleep,
	Whiles thou art waking.
SEBASTIAN	Thou dost snore distinctly:
	There's meaning in thy snores.
ANTONIO	If you but knew
	How you the purpose cherish whiles thus you mock it!
	Although this lord of weak remembrance here
	Professes to persuade the King his son's alive,
	'Tis as impossible that he's undrown'd
	As he that sleeps here swims.
SEBASTIAN	I have no hope
	That he's undrown'd.
ANTONIO	O, out of that "no hope"
	What great hope have you! Will you grant with me
	That Ferdinand is drown'd?
SEBASTIAN	He's gone.
ANTONIO	Then tell me
	Who's the next heir of Naples?
SEBASTIAN	Claribel.
ANTONIO	She that is Queen of Tunis; she that dwells
	Ten leagues beyond man's life. Say this were death
	That now hath seiz'd them, why they were no worse
	Than now they are; there be that can rule Naples
	As well as he that sleeps. O that you bore
	The mind that I do! What a sleep were this

18

	For your advancement! Do you understand me?
SEBASTIAN	Methinks I do. Moreover, I remember
	You did supplant your brother Prospero.
	But for your conscience —
ANTONIO	Ay, sir; where lies that? Here lies your brother,
	No better than the earth he lies upon,
	If he were that which now he's like — that's dead —
	Whom I with this obedient steel — three inches of it —
	Can lay to bed for ever; whiles you, doing thus,
	To the perpetual wink for aye might put
	This ancient morsel, this Sir Prudence. The rest,
	They'll tell the clock to any business that
	We say befits the hour.
SEBASTIAN	Thy case, dear friend,
	Shall be my precedent: as thou got'st Milan
	I'll come by Naples. Draw thy sword; one stroke
	Shall free thee from the tribute which thou payest,
	And I the King shall love thee.
ANTONIO	Draw together;
	And when I rear my hand do you the like,
	To fall on Gonzalo.
SEBASTIAN	O, but one word.
	They talk apart. Enter Ariel with music and song.
ARIEL	My master through his art foresees the danger.
	Sings in Gonzalo's ear.
	While you here do snoring lie,
	Open-ey'd Conspiracy
	His time doth take.
	If of life you keep a care,
	Shake off slumber and beware.
	Awake, awake!
ANTONIO	Then let us both be sudden.
	Antonio and Sebastian draw their swords.
GONZALO	*Wakes.* Now, good angels preserve the King! *He shakes Alonso.*
ALONSO	Why, how now? Ho! Awake? Why are you drawn?
	Wherefore this ghastly looking?
GONZALO	What's the matter?
SEBASTIAN	Whiles we stood here securing your repose —
	Even now — we heard a hollow burst of bellowing
	Like bulls, or rather lions — did 't not wake you?
ANTONIO	O, 'twas a din to fright a monster's ear,
	To make an earthquake!
ALONSO	Heard you this, Gonzalo?
GONZALO	Upon mine honor, sir, I heard a humming —

19

And that a strange one too — which did awake me.
Methinks 'tis best we stand upon our guard,
Or that we quit this place. Let's draw our weapons.

ALONSO   And let's make further search for my poor son.
ARIEL   Prospero, my lord, shall know what I have done.
           So, King, go safely on to seek thy son.   *Exeunt.*

Scene 3

*Caliban is Prospero's slave, but an unwilling one. Prospero
controls him by setting spirits to punish him if he does wrong.
When, therefore, Caliban sees a strange creature coming toward
him, he assumes it is a spirit and falls to the ground hoping he
will not be noticed. This "spirit" is actually the King's jester
Trinculo. Furthermore, not one but two "spirits" arrive, one
after the other. Trinculo is first on the scene; seeing no other*

20

shelter from the storm that is brewing, he crawls under Caliban's cloak (his gabardine). Then Stephano comes along singing to keep his spirits up. By now Caliban is quaking under his gabardine, scared out of whatever wits he has by these two spirits. Trinculo, also under the gabardine, is quaking too; when he hears the voice of his drowned friend Stephano, he is sure he has fallen into the hands of devils. Stephano comes upon this freak with four legs and two heads and immediately has the same thought Trinculo had had: he will do as many travelers did with the strange creatures they found, and will take the monster home, exhibit him, and thereby make his fortune. First he tries to revive the monster by giving each of its heads a taste from his bottle. In so doing he discovers his shipmate Trinculo —and makes poor Caliban think him a god, who has such heavenly liquor.

Enter Caliban with a burthen of wood. A noise of thunder heard.

CALIBAN   All the infections that the sun sucks up
From bogs, fens, flats on Prosper fall, and make him
By inchmeal a disease! His spirits hear me,
And yet I needs must curse. But they'll nor pinch,
Nor pitch me i' th' mire, unless he bid 'em.
Enter Trinculo.
Here comes a spirit of his, and to torment me
For bringing wood in slowly! I'll fall flat.
Perchance he will not mind me.

TRINCULO   Here's neither bush nor shrub to bear off any weather at all, and another storm brewing. If it should thunder, as it did before, I know not where to hide my head. Yond same cloud cannot choose but fall by pailfuls. What have we here, a man? or a fish? Dead or alive? A fish. He smells like a fish. A strange fish! Were I in England now and had but this fish, not a holiday fool there but would give a piece of silver. When they will not give a doit to relieve a lame beggar, they will lay out ten to see a dead Indian. Legg'd like a man, and his fins like arms! Warm, o' my troth! This is no fish but an islander, that hath lately suffered by a thunderbolt. *Thunder.* Alas! The storm is come again! My best way is to creep under his gabardine: there is no other shelter hereabout. Misery acquaints a man with strange bedfellows! *Creeps under Caliban's garment.*
Enter Stephano singing.

STEPHANO   I shall no more to sea, to sea;
    Here shall I die ashore.
This is a very scurvy tune to sing at a man's funeral! Well, here's

21

my comfort. *Drinks and then sings.*

> The master, the swabber, the boatswain, and I,
> The gunner and his mate
> Lov'd Moll, Meg, and Marian, and Margery,
> But none of us car'd for Kate.
> For she had a tongue with a tang,
> Would cry to a sailor, "Go hang!"
> She lov'd not the savor of tar nor of pitch,
> Yet a tailor might scratch her where'er she did itch.
> Then to sea, boys, and let her go hang!

This is a scurvy tune, too: but here's my comfort. *Drinks.*

CALIBAN   Do not torment me! O!

STEPHANO   What's the matter? Have we devils here? Ha? I have not 'scap'd drowning to be afeard now of your four legs.

CALIBAN   The spirit torments me! O!

STEPHANO   This is some monster of the isle with four legs, who hath got — as I take it — an ague. Where the devil should he learn our language?

CALIBAN   Do not torment me, prithee! I'll bring my wood home faster.

STEPHANO   He's in his fit now, and does not talk after the wisest. He shall taste of my bottle! It will go near to remove his fit. If I can recover him and keep him tame, I will not take too much for him; he shall pay for him that hath him, and that soundly.

CALIBAN	Thou dost me yet but little hurt. Thou wilt anon; I know it by thy trembling.
STEPHANO	Open your mouth! This will shake your shaking, I can tell you, and that soundly. *Gives Caliban drink.*
TRINCULO	I should know that voice! It should be — but he is drown'd, and these are devils. O defend me!
STEPHANO	Four legs and two voices — a most delicate monster! If all the wine in my bottle will recover him, I will help his ague. Come! I will pour some in thy other mouth.
TRINCULO	Stephano!
STEPHANO	Doth thy other mouth call me? Mercy, mercy! This is a devil and no monster! I will leave him!
TRINCULO	Stephano! If thou beest Stephano, touch me and speak to me, for I am Trinculo — be not afeard — thy good friend Trinculo.
STEPHANO	If thou beest Trinculo, come forth! I'll pull thee by the lesser legs . . . Thou art very Trinculo indeed! How cam'st thou to be the siege of this mooncalf?
TRINCULO	I took him to be kill'd with a thunderstroke. But art thou not drown'd, Stephano? I hope now thou art not drown'd! O Stephano, two Neopolitans 'scap'd?
STEPHANO	Prithee do not turn me about — my stomach is not constant.
CALIBAN	These be fine things an if they be not sprites! That's a brave god, and bears celestial liquor. I will kneel to him.
STEPHANO	How didst thou 'scape? How cam'st thou hither? Swear by this bottle how thou cam'st hither! I escap'd upon a butt of sack which the sailors heaved o'erboard.
CALIBAN	I'll swear upon that bottle to be thy true subject, for the liquor is not earthly.
STEPHANO	Here! Swear then how thou escap'dst.
TRINCULO	Swum ashore, man, like a duck!
STEPHANO	Here, kiss the book. *Trinculo drinks.* Though thou canst swim like a duck, thou art made like a goose.
CALIBAN	Hast thou not dropp'd from heaven?
STEPHANO	Out o' th' moon, I do assure thee. I was the man i' th' moon, when time was.
CALIBAN	I have seen thee in her — and I do adore thee!
TRINCULO	This is a very shallow monster! The man i' th' moon? A most poor credulous monster!
CALIBAN	I'll show thee every fertile inch o' th' island — and I will kiss thy foot! I prithee, be my god.
TRINCULO	I shall laugh myself to death at this puppy-headed monster!
CALIBAN	I'll show thee the best springs; I'll pluck thee berries; I'll fish for thee, and get thee wood enough. A plague upon the tyrant that I serve! I'll bear him no more sticks, but follow thee,

	Thou wondrous man. I'll swear myself thy subject.
STEPHANO	I prithee now, lead the way without any more talking. Trinculo, the King and all our company else being drown'd, we will inherit here.
CALIBAN	*Sings drunkenly.*

Farewell, master; farewell, farewell!

| TRINCULO | A howling monster! a drunken monster! |
| CALIBAN | No more dams I'll make for fish, |

Nor fetch in firing
At requiring,
Nor scrape trenchering, nor wash dish.
'Ban, 'Ban, Ca-Caliban
Has a new master — get a new man.

Freedom, hey-day! hey-day, freedom! freedom, hey-day, freedom!

| STEPHANO | O brave monster! lead the way.   *Exeunt.* |

ACT II
———
Scene 1

All the action in this play takes place within a single afternoon. It was after two o'clock when Ariel first reported to Prospero how he had disposed of the ship and brought the passengers safely to land. Prospero intends to torment his enemies for a few hours only; by six o'clock it will all be over. But for this one afternoon they will truly believe themselves to be on the Iland of Divels.

	Enter Ferdinand, bearing a log.
FERDINAND	There be some sports are painful, and their labor

Delight in them sets off. This my mean task
Would be as heavy to me as odious, but
The mistress which I serve quickens what's dead
And makes my labors pleasures. O she is
Ten times more gentle than her father's crabbed,
And he's compos'd of harshness. My sweet mistress
Weeps when she sees me work.
Enter Miranda, and Prospero unseen.

| MIRANDA | Alas, now pray you |

Work not so hard! I would the lightning had

Burnt up those logs that you are enjoin'd to pile:
Pray rest yourself. My father is hard at study:
He's safe for these three hours.

FERDINAND   O most dear mistress,
The sun will set before I shall discharge
What I must strive to do.

MIRANDA   If you'll sit down
I'll bear your logs the while.

FERDINAND   No, precious creature,
I had rather crack my sinews, break my back,
Than you should such dishonor undergo
While I sit lazy by. I do beseech you,
What is your name?

MIRANDA   Miranda.

FERDINAND   Admir'd Miranda,
So perfect and so peerless. Hear my soul speak:
The very instant that I saw you did
My heart fly to your service; for your sake
Am I this patient log-man.

MIRANDA   Do you love me?

FERDINAND   Beyond all limit of what else i' th' world,
I do love, prize, honor you.

MIRANDA   Hence, bashful cunning,
And prompt me, plain and holy innocence.
I am your wife if you will marry me;
If not I'll die your maid.

FERDINAND   My mistress, dearest!
And I thus humble ever.

MIRANDA   My husband, then?

FERDINAND   Ay, with a heart as willing
As bondage e'er of freedom! Here's my hand.

MIRANDA   And mine, with my heart in 't; and now farewell
Till half an hour hence.   *Exeunt Ferdinand and Miranda.*

PROSPERO   Heavens rain grace
On that which breeds between 'em.   *Exit.*

Scene 2

Enter Caliban, Stephano, and Trinculo.

STEPHANO   Servant-monster, thy eyes are almost set in thy head.
TRINCULO   He were a brave monster indeed if they were set in his tail.

CALIBAN	I'll not serve him — *Points to Trinculo.* He is not valiant.
TRINCULO	Thou liest, most ignorant monster! I am in case to justle a constable! Wilt thou tell a monstrous lie, being but half a fish and half a monster?
CALIBAN	Lo, how he mocks me! Wilt thou let him, my lord?
TRINCULO	"Lord," quoth he?
STEPHANO	Trinculo, keep a good tongue in your head! The poor monster's my subject and he shall not suffer indignity.
CALIBAN	I thank my noble lord. Wilt thou be pleas'd to hearken once again to the suit I made to thee?
STEPHANO	Marry will I. Kneel and repeat it. *Enter Ariel, invisible.*
CALIBAN	As I told thee before, I am subject to a tyrant, a sorcerer, that by his cunning hath cheated me of the island.
ARIEL	*Mimicking Trinculo's voice.* Thou liest.
CALIBAN	*To Trinculo.* Thou liest, thou jesting monkey, thou! I do not lie.
STEPHANO	Trinculo, if you trouble him any more in 's tale, by this hand I will supplant some of your teeth.
TRINCULO	Why, I said nothing.
STEPHANO	Mum, then, and no more! *To Caliban.* Proceed.
CALIBAN	I say by sorcery he got this isle — From me, he got it. If thy greatness will Revenge it on him — for I know thou dar'st — Thou shalt be lord of it, and I'll serve thee.
STEPHANO	Canst thou bring me to the party?
CALIBAN	Yea, yea, my lord, I'll yield him thee asleep, Where thou may'st knock a nail into his head.
ARIEL	*In Trinculo's voice.* Thou liest. Thou canst not.
CALIBAN	Thou scurvy patch! I do beseech thy greatness, give him blows And take his bottle from him!
TRINCULO	Why what did I? I did nothing!
STEPHANO	Didst thou not say he lied?
ARIEL	*In Trinculo's voice.* Thou liest.
STEPHANO	Do I so? Take thou that! *Hits Trinculo.* As you like this, give me the lie another time.
TRINCULO	I did not give the lie! Out o' your wits, and hearing too?
CALIBAN	Beat him enough! After a little time I'll beat him too.
STEPHANO	*To Trinculo.* Stand farther off! *To Caliban.* Come, proceed.
CALIBAN	Why, as I told thee, 'tis a custom with him I' th' afternoon to sleep; there thou mayst brain him, Having first seiz'd his books, or with a log Batter his skull, or paunch him with a stake, Or cut his wezand with thy knife. Remember

	First to possess his books, for without them
	He's but a sot, as I am, nor hath not
	One spirit to command. Burn but his books.
STEPHANO	Monster, I will kill this man! His daughter and I will be King and Queen, and Trinculo and thyself shall be viceroys! Dost thou like the plot, Trinculo?
TRINCULO	Excellent.
STEPHANO	Give me thy hand; I am sorry I beat thee.
ARIEL	This will I tell my master.
CALIBAN	Thou mak'st me merry: I am full of pleasure; Let us be jocund. Will you troll the catch You taught me but whilere?
STEPHANO	At thy request, monster, I will do reason, any reason. Come on, Trinculo, let us sing.

    Flout 'em and scout 'em —
    And scout 'em, and flout 'em;
    Thought is free.

CALIBAN	That's not the tune.

Ariel plays the tune on a tabor and pipe.

STEPHANO	What is this same?
TRINCULO	This is the tune of our catch, play'd by the picture of No-body.
STEPHANO	O forgive me my sins!
TRINCULO	Mercy upon us!
CALIBAN	Art thou afeard?
STEPHANO	No, monster, not I.
CALIBAN	Be not afeard, the isle is full of noises, Sounds and sweet airs that give delight and hurt not. Sometimes a thousand twangling instruments Will hum about mine ears, and sometimes voices That if I then had wak'd after long sleep Will make me sleep again; and then in dreaming The clouds methought would open and show riches Ready to drop upon me, that when I wak'd I cried to dream again.
TRINCULO	The sound is going away. Let's follow it and after do our work. *Exeunt.*

Scene 3

Enter Alonso, Sebastian, Antonio, Gonzalo, Adrian, Francisco, and others.

27

GONZALO	By'r lakin, I can go no further, sir.
	I needs must rest me.
ALONSO	Old lord, I cannot blame thee
	Who am myself attach'd with weariness.
	Even here I will put off my hope: he is drown'd
	Whom thus we stray to find, and the sea mocks
	Our frustrate search on land. Well, let him go.
ANTONIO	*To Sebastian.* Do not for one repulse forgo the purpose
	That you resolv'd t' effect.
SEBASTIAN	The next advantage
	Will we take throughly.
ANTONIO	Let it be tonight.

Solemn and strange music; enter Prospero above invisible.

ALONSO	What harmony is this? My good friends, hark!
GONZALO	Marvelous sweet music.

Enter several strange shapes bringing in a banquet, and dance about it with gentle actions of salutations; inviting the King, etc., to eat, they depart.

ALONSO	Give us kind keepers, heavens! What were these?
SEBASTIAN	Now I'll believe that there are unicorns!
ANTONIO	And what does else want credit, come to me
	And I'll be sworn 'tis true! Travelers ne'er did lie,
	Though fools at home condemn 'em.
GONZALO	If in Naples
	I should report this now, would they believe me?
FRANCISCO	They vanish'd strangely.
SEBASTIAN	No matter, since
	They have left their viands behind, for we have stomachs.
	Will 't please you taste of what is here?
ALONSO	Not I.
GONZALO	Faith, sir, you need not fear such things as these.

Thunder and lightning. Enter Ariel like a harpy, claps his wings, and with a quaint device the banquet vanishes.

ARIEL	You are three men of sin, whom destiny
	The never-surfeited sea hath caus'd to belch up
	On this isle.

Alonso, Sebastian, and Antonio draw their swords.

	You fools! The elements
	Of whom your swords are temper'd may as well
	Wound the loud winds, or with bemock'd-at stabs
	Kill the still closing waters as diminish
	One dowl that's in my plume! But remember —
	For that's my business to you — that you three
	From Milan did supplant good Prospero,
	Expos'd unto the sea — which hath requit it —

Him and his innocent child; for which foul deed
The powers, delaying — not forgetting — have
Incens'd the seas and shores. Thee of thy son
They have bereft and do pronounce by me:
Ling'ring perdition shall step by step attend
You and your ways, whose wraths to guard you from —
Which here in this most desolate isle else falls
Upon your heads — is nothing but heart's sorrow
And a clear life ensuing.   *Vanishes in thunder.*

PROSPERO   My high charms work,
And these mine enemies, are all knit up
In their distractions; and in these fits I leave them.   *Exit.*

GONZALO   I' th' name of something holy, sir, why stand you
In this strange stare?

ALONSO   O, it is monstrous, monstrous!
Methought the billows spoke and told me of it;
The winds did sing it to me, and the thunder —
That deep and dreadful organ pipe — pronounc'd
The name of Prosper.   *Exit.*

SEBASTIAN   But one fiend at a time —
I'll fight their legions o'er!

ANTONIO   I'll be thy second.
                         Exeunt Sebastian and Antonio.

GONZALO   All three of them are desperate! Their great guilt,
Like poison given to work a great time after,
Now 'gins to bite the spirits. Follow them swiftly
And hinder them from what this ecstasy
May now provoke them to.

ADRIAN   Follow, I pray you.   *Exeunt omnes.*

Scene 4

*It is time for Prospero to finish his work. In his hands he holds
the fate of everyone on the island. His enemies Antonio and
Alonso are now in a frenzy of fear and guilt, haunted by spirits
and pursued by demons. Caliban and his two villainous com-
panions were led by Ariel into a stagnant pool covered with
green slime, from which they will soon emerge, dripping, stink-*

ing, and exasperated. And Ferdinand, the young, the brave, the handsome, is valiantly piling logs for his Miranda. What will their fates be?

Enter Prospero, Ferdinand, and Miranda.

PROSPERO

If I have too austerely punish'd you
Your compensation makes amends, for I
Have given you here a third of mine own life,
Or that for which I live; all thy vexations
Were but my trials of thy love, and thou
Hast strangely stood the test. Here, afore heaven,
Then, as my gift and thine own acquisition
Worthily purchas'd, take my daughter. Go
Sit then and talk with her; she is thine own.

        Exeunt Ferdinand and Miranda.

What, Ariel! Come with a thought! Ariel: Come!
Enter Ariel.

ARIEL

Thy thoughts I cleave to. What's thy pleasure?

PROSPERO

            Spirit,
We must prepare to meet with Caliban.

ARIEL

Ay, my commander.

PROSPERO

      Where didst thou leave these varlets?

ARIEL

I' th' filthy mantled pool beyond your cell,
There dancing up to th' chins.

PROSPERO

        Well done, my bird.
The trumpery in my house, go bring it hither
For stale to catch these thieves.

ARIEL

        I go, I go.   *Exit.*

PROSPERO

A devil, a born devil, on whom my pains,
Humanely taken, all, all lost, quite lost,
And as with age his body uglier grows,
So his mind cankers.
Enter Ariel, loaden with glistering apparel.
     Come, hang them here.
Enter Caliban, Stephano, and Trinculo all wet.

CALIBAN

Pray you, tread softly, that the blind mole may not hear a footfall: we now are near his cell.

STEPHANO

Monster, your fairy, which you say is a harmless fairy, has done little better than play'd the Jack with us. If I should take a displeasure against you — look you.

TRINCULO

Thou wert but a lost monster.

CALIBAN

Good my lord, give me thy favor still.
Be patient, for the prize I'll bring thee to
Shall hoodwink this mischance. Therefore speak softly.

TRINCULO

Ay, but to lose our bottles in the pool!

STEPHANO	There is not only disgrace and dishonor in that, monster, but an infinite loss.
CALIBAN	Prithee, my King, be quiet. Seest thou here, This is the mouth o' th' cell! No noise and enter.
STEPHANO	I do begin to have bloody thoughts.
TRINCULO	O King Stephano, O peer! O worthy Stephano! Look what a wardrobe here is for thee!
CALIBAN	Let it alone, thou fool, it is but trash.
TRINCULO	Oho, monster! We know what belongs to a frippery. O King Stephano!
STEPHANO	Put off that gown, Trinculo. By this hand, I'll have that gown!
CALIBAN	The dropsy drown this fool! What do you mean To dote thus on such luggage? Let's all on And do the murther first. If he awake —
STEPHANO	Be quiet, monster.
CALIBAN	We shall lose our time And all be turn'd to barnacles, or to apes With foreheads villainous low.
STEPHANO	Monster, help to bear this away where my hogshead of wine is, or I'll turn you out of my kingdom! Go to, carry this.
TRINCULO	And this.
STEPHANO	Ay, and this.

A noise of hunters heard. Enter divers spirits in shape of dogs and hounds, hunting them about, Prospero and Ariel setting them on.

PROSPERO	Hey, Mountain, hey!
ARIEL	Silver! There it goes, Silver!
PROSPERO	Fury, Fury! There, Tyrant, there! Hark, hark!

Exeunt all but Prospero and Ariel.

	Let them be hunted soundly!
ARIEL	Hark, they roar!
PROSPERO	Now does my project gather to a head;
	My charms crack not, my spirits all obey.
	How fares the King and 's followers?
ARIEL	The King,
	His brother, and yours, abide all three distracted,
	And the remainder mourning over them
	Brimful of sorrow and dismay, but chiefly
	Him that you term'd, sir, the good old lord, Gonzalo.
	His tears run down his beard like winter's drops
	From eaves of reeds. Your charm so strongly works 'em
	That if you now beheld them, your affections
	Would become tender.
PROSPERO	Dost thou think so, spirit?
ARIEL	Mine would, sir, were I human.
PROSPERO	And mine shall.
	Hast thou — which art but air — a touch, a feeling
	Of their afflictions, and shall not myself,
	One of their kind, be kindlier mov'd than thou art?
	My charms I'll break, their senses I'll restore,
	And they shall be themselves.
ARIEL	I'll fetch them, sir. *Exit.*

Before the final confrontation with his brother and Alonso, Prospero vows to give up forever the practice of magic. He will break his wand, sink his books in the sea, and free the spirits who have served him. Then finally he reveals himself to the spellbound prisoners and all ends happily. Prospero regains his dukedom, which he is now prepared to govern wisely, the wicked repent and are forgiven, and the happy lovers receive the King's blessing. As his last service Ariel promises them fair weather and fresh breezes for a speedy voyage home to Italy.

PROSPERO	Ye elves of hills, brooks, standing lakes, and groves,
	And ye that on the sands with printless foot
	Do chase the ebbing Neptune and do fly him
	When he comes back; by your aid I have bedimm'd
	The noontide sun, call'd forth the mutinous winds,
	And 'twixt the green sea and the azur'd vault
	Set roaring war. But this rough magic now

I here abjure, and when I have requir'd
Some heavenly music, I'll break my staff,
Bury it certain fathoms in the earth,
And deeper than did ever plummet sound
I'll drown my book.

Here enters Ariel singing, then Alonso, with a frantic gesture,
attended by Gonzalo; Sebastian and Antonio in like manner at-
tended by Adrian and Francisco. They all enter the circle which
Prospero has made and there stand charm'd.

ARIEL
    Where the bee sucks, there suck I;
    In a cowslip's bell I lie;
    There I couch when owls do cry;
    On the bat's back I do fly
      After summer merrily.
    Merrily, merrily shall I live now
    Under the blossom that hangs on the bough.

PROSPERO
Why that's my dainty Ariel! I shall miss thee,
But yet thou shalt have freedom.   *Exit Ariel.*

GONZALO
All torment, trouble, wonder, and amazement
Inhabits here! Some heavenly power guide us
Out of this fearful country!

PROSPERO
                  Behold, Sir King,
The wronged Duke of Milan, Prospero!
For more assurance that a living prince
Does now speak to thee, I embrace thy body,
And to thee and thy company I bid
A hearty welcome.

ALONSO
                Whe'r thou beest he or no,
Or some enchanted trifle to abuse me —
As late I have been — I not know. If this be,
Thy dukedom I resign and do entreat
Thou pardon me my wrongs.

PROSPERO
To Gonzalo.   First, noble friend,
Let me embrace thine age, whose honor cannot
Be measur'd or confin'd.

GONZALO
                Whether this be
Or be not I'll not swear.

PROSPERO
                You do yet taste
Some subtleties o' th' isle, that will not let you
Believe things certain. Welcome, my friends all,
To Sebastian and Antonio.
But you, my brace of lords; were I so minded
I could justify you traitors! At this time
I will tell no tales.

SEBASTIAN
           The devil speaks in him!

PROSPERO	For you, most wicked brother, I do forgive Thy rankest fault — all of them — and require My dukedom of thee.
ALONSO	If thou beest Prospero Give us particulars of thy preservation, How thou hast met us here who three hours since Were wreck'd upon this shore, where I have lost My dear son Ferdinand.
PROSPERO	I am woe for 't, sir. Yet must content me with like loss, for I Have lost my daughter.
ALONSO	A daughter? O heavens that they were living both in Naples, The King and Queen there! When did you lose your daughter?
PROSPERO	In this last tempest. I perceive these lords Scarce think their eyes do offices of truth. But I am Prospero and that very Duke Which was thrust forth of Milan. Welcome, sir. This cell's my court; here have I few attendants, And subjects none abroad; pray you look in. My dukedom since you have given me again, I will requite you with as good a thing. *Prospero discloses Ferdinand and Miranda, playing at chess.*
ALONSO	If this prove A vision of the island, one dear son Shall I twice lose.
SEBASTIAN	A most high miracle.
FERDINAND	*Seeing Alonso.* Though the seas threaten, they are merciful. I have curs'd them without cause.
MIRANDA	O wonder! How many goodly creatures are there here! How beauteous mankind is! O brave new world That has such people in 't!
PROSPERO	'Tis new to thee.
ALONSO	What is this maid, with whom thou wast at play? Is she the goddess that hath sever'd us And brought us thus together?
FERDINAND	Sir, she is mortal, But by immortal Providence she's mine. I chose her when I could not ask my father For his advice — nor thought I had one. She Is daughter to this famous Duke of Milan, Of whom so often I have heard renown But never saw before, of whom I have Receiv'd a second life; and second father

	This lady makes him to me.
ALONSO	I am hers.
GONZALO	Was Milan thrust from Milan, that his issue
	Should become Kings of Naples? O rejoice
	Beyond a common joy. In one voyage
	Did Claribel her husband find at Tunis,
	And Ferdinand, her brother, found a wife
	Where he himself was lost; Prospero his dukedom
	In a poor isle; and all of us ourselves,
	When no man was his own.
ALONSO	Give me your hands.
	Let grief and sorrow still embrace his heart
	That doth not wish you joy.
GONZALO	Be it so, amen!

Enter Ariel, with the Master and Boatswain amazedly following.

	O look, sir, look, sir, here is more of us!
	I prophesied if a gallows were on land
	This fellow could not drown! What is the news?
BOATSWAIN	The best news is that we have safely found
	Our King and company; the next, our ship
	Is tight and yare, and bravely rigg'd as when
	We first put out to sea.
ARIEL	*To Prospero.* Was 't well done?
PROSPERO	Bravely, my diligence; thou shalt be free.
	Set Caliban and his companions free:
	Untie the spell. *Exit Ariel.*
	How fares my gracious sir?
	There are yet missing of your company
	Some few odd lads that you remember not.

*Enter Ariel, driving in Caliban, Stephano, and Trinculo, in their
stolen apparel.*

TRINCULO	If these be true spies which I wear in my head, here's a goodly sight.
SEBASTIAN	What things are these, my Lord Antonio?
PROSPERO	These three have robb'd me, and this demi-devil,
	For he's a bastard one, had plotted with them
	To take my life. Two of these fellows you
	Must know and own, this thing of darkness I
	Acknowledge mine.
CALIBAN	I shall be pinch'd to death.
ALONSO	Is not this Stephano, my drunken butler?
STEPHANO	I am not Stephano, but a cramp.
ALONSO	This is a strange thing as e'er I look'd on.
PROSPERO	He is as disproportion'd in his manners
	As in his shape! Go, sirrah, to my cell;

	Take with you your companions — as you look
	To have my pardon, trim it handsomely.
CALIBAN	Ay, that I will! What a thrice-double ass
	Was I to take this drunkard for a god
	And worship this dull fool!
PROSPERO	Go to, away!

Exeunt Caliban, Stephano, and Trinculo.

Sir, I invite your Highness and your train
To my poor cell, where you shall take your rest.

ALONSO I long to hear the story of your life.

PROSPERO Please you draw near. I shall deliver all,
And promise you calm seas, auspicious gales,
And sail so expeditious that shall catch
Your royal fleet far off. My Ariel, chick,
That is thy charge — then to the elements
Be free, and fare thou well!   *Exeunt all but Prospero.*
Our revels now are ended: these our actors
Are melted into air, into thin air;
And like the baseless fabric of this vision
The cloud-capp'd towers, the gorgeous palaces,
The solemn temples, the great globe itself,
Yea, all which it inherit, shall dissolve
And like this insubstantial pageant faded
Leave not a rack behind: we are such stuff
As dreams are made on, and our little life
Is rounded with a sleep.   *Exit.*

2

A Midsummer Night's Dream

Village Greens and Theaters

2

IN SHAKESPEARE'S TIME jugglers and acrobats, minstrels and bands of actors wandered over England, as they had been doing for hundreds of years. They performed wherever they could gather a small crowd, much as an organ-grinder and his monkey entertain children today. They entertained lords and ladies in the castles, and townsmen in the village squares. These traveling bands of players usually consisted of four or five men, with a boy to play women's parts. Because actors were thought of as being little better than petty criminals — tramps, beggars, and pickpockets — they were liable to arrest for vagrancy, or worse, in any towns they visited. In order to avoid this danger they liked to attach themselves to some nobleman's household, so they could be legally classified as his servants, which gave them in effect a license to practice their art. Shakespeare's company was known for many years as the Lord Chamberlain's Men until King James made them the King's Majesty's Servants in 1603.

The actors presented their plays wherever they could, in schools, town halls, or even on street corners. If a town was large enough, it probably boasted an arena for bearbaiting or bullbaiting, very popular but cruel amusements in which bulls or bears were chained to posts and then attacked by dogs. Such an arena served admirably as a theater. Another favorite place for a performance was the yard of an inn. Most inns of the sixteenth century were built in the form of a hollow rectangle, two or three stories high. The rooms of the inn opened onto galleries that surrounded a courtyard in the center. By erecting a platform at one end of the yard, an adequate theater was produced. The players could use the rooms immediately behind the platform as dressing rooms, and a portion of the second-floor gallery above might even be called into use occasionally to represent an upper room or a castle wall. Poor members of the audience paid a penny or two to stand in the yard around the platform (and were consequently called the "groundlings"); the more wealthy sat on stools in the open galleries.

When the first theaters were built in England toward the end of the sixteenth century, the inns and arenas were adopted as models. Most of the theaters were octagonal in shape, like the arenas; one, the Fortune, was square like the inn yards. The Hope Theatre was designed with a removable stage in order to accommodate both plays and bullbaiting. Unfortunately, very little is actually known about these theaters. The only explicit information available today is one contemporary sketch of the inside of a theater, a few sketches of London showing outside views of several theaters, and contracts for building two theaters which, sad to relate, leave most details unspecified, saying only that something is to be built as it is in some already completed theater, or that it is to be built according to an accompanying plan, which has been lost. With only this to go on many men have tried diligently to reconstruct the theater Shakespeare wrote for. There are a few things on which there is general agreement: Just as the audience stood, or sat, around three or possibly all four sides of the platform in the inn yards and arenas, so in the theaters. Just as there was no roof over the arena or the inn courtyard, so there was none over the center area of the theaters; there was a roof over part of the stage and over the surrounding balconies, but if a sudden rainstorm arose, the groundlings were sure to get wet. In these public theaters performances were always given in the afternoon. They were announced by raising a flag over the theater on the day of the performance.

Such was the theater that Shakespeare wrote for. His plays were written to be played without intermission, the scenes following quickly one after another. On Shakespeare's stage there was almost no scenery to indicate place and no elaborate lighting effects to indicate time. Shakespeare sets the scene with the words his characters speak. He leaves our imaginations free to create sunny days and stormy nights, primeval forests or city streets, a village inn or the castle of a king.

The sixteenth and early seventeenth centuries were busy times theatrically. There were many groups of professional actors performing in the theaters of London or traveling around from town to town. Among them were some very popular companies of boy actors. These companies had started as boys' choirs at great cathedrals and at the court. The boys were trained in schools set up by the chapels, and they acted in small private theaters attended by members of the aristocracy. In addition to these professional actors, there were active amateur groups at England's two great universities, Oxford and Cambridge, and at the Inns of Court (the law schools) in London. There students were busily producing witty interludes and imitations of Latin comedies. Outside London, people in the towns and villages were producing plays, too — often crude, but always lively.

Much earlier, during the Middle Ages, the church had adopted a custom of celebrating religious festivals by presenting Bible stories and moral teachings in the form of plays. The plays were of three kinds: Miracle plays showed the lives of the saints; Mysteries told stories from the Bible; and Moralities showed the struggle between good and bad within a man, with characters called Vice, Good Deeds, Knowledge, and so on. Gradually, through the years, the townsmen took this function over from the churches. From very simple dramatizations showing the birth of Christ at Christmas, or the resurrection at Easter, the productions grew to be elaborate cycles of plays that sometimes covered the time from the creation of the world to the last judgment. Each of the trade guilds of a town was responsible for an incident in the cycle; the shipwright's guild, for example, would tell the story of the building of the Ark. Each play was presented on its own stage, called a pageant, which was mounted on wheels and could be moved from street to street in the town. Thus, the audience could stay in one place and have all the plays in a cycle brought to them, one after another. The plays were based on Bible stories, but as the church's part in the production became less, the amount of nonreligious material increased. Eventually the plays were full of earthy jokes and comical situations. In a play about the shepherds keeping watch over their flocks by night, one shepherd stole a sheep from the others. He hid the sheep in bed with his wife and pretended it was their newborn baby. Imagine for yourself the furor when the "baby" said "Baa-a-a"!

These Miracle or Morality plays were the high points of the year and were regular events. The delight in them created a demand for more dramatic entertainment, and interludes satisfied that demand. An interlude was a short play that could be played by a few actors without much scenery. It was the interludes that the traveling players and bands of minstrels took from town to town. Frequently, too, local guilds or the resident players at a court composed interludes in honor of some special event, such as a visit from the Queen, the birth of a nobleman's child, or a royal marriage.

And so we come to *A Midsummer Night's Dream*. The "rude mechanicals" (rough, ignorant workingmen) of Athens compose a play in honor of the wedding of their ruler, Theseus. When we watch them in their play, we are seeing what a person of the sixteenth century would have seen at a village fair, ordinary people in a sincere but very amateurish performance of a crude play they wrote themselves. As a matter of fact, when we see the Duke and the other Athenians we see what Englishmen would expect to see: people just like themselves. Shakespeare has not tried to make his characters act or talk the way citizens of ancient Athens might act or talk. Instead they act very much the way Englishmen — common workmen or aristocratic gentlemen — would act, and think what they would think. But they talk as only Shakespeare could make them talk.

A Midsummer Night's Dream

2

The Characters:

THESEUS, Duke of Athens
EGEUS, father of Hermia
LYSANDER, in love with Hermia
DEMETRIUS, also in love with Hermia
PHILOSTRATE, Master of the Revels to Theseus
QUINCE, a carpenter (Prologue in the interlude)
BOTTOM, a weaver (Pyramus in the interlude)
FLUTE, a bellows-mender (Thisby in the interlude)
SNOUT, a tinker (Wall in the interlude)
SNUG, a joiner (Lion in the interlude)
STARVELING, a tailor (Moonshine in the interlude)
HIPPOLYTA, Queen of the Amazons, betrothed to Theseus
HERMIA, in love with Lysander
HELENA, in love with Demetrius
OBERON, King of the Fairies
TITANIA, Queen of the Fairies
PUCK, or Robin Goodfellow
PEASEBLOSSOM, a fairy
COBWEB, a fairy
MOTH, a fairy
MUSTARDSEED, a fairy
OTHER FAIRIES, attending Oberon and Titania
ATTENDANTS ON THESEUS AND HIPPOLYTA

The Scene: Athens and a wood nearby

The heart of this play is the moonstruck madness that goes on one summer night in a magical forest somewhere, supposedly, in ancient Greece. That enchanted night is framed between two scenes at the palace of Theseus, the mythical ruler of

Athens who solved the mystery of the Minotaur. These two scenes are essentially Prologue (to give some of the threads to be used in weaving the plot) and Epilogue (to tie them all up neatly at the end).

The Prologue and Epilogue tell the story of the marriage of Theseus (here called a Duke) to Hippolyta, the Queen of the Amazons, a mythical race of warrior women. All Athens will celebrate the marriage with feasting and merriment.

Actually, there is nothing about the play that is Grecian except the names of some of the characters. But setting it in ancient Greece helps to create an atmosphere of long-ago-and-faraway, where almost anything can, and does, happen.

Scene 1

The happy mood with which the play starts is broken almost immediately by a father who is much displeased that his daughter Hermia will not consent to marry Demetrius, the man he has picked out for her. There is a cruel law in Athens which says that a father has the right to put to death a disobedient child. Egeus invokes this law, and the Duke has no choice except to enforce it. Sadly he gives Hermia four days to make up her mind to obey her father; if she does not, she must be sentenced to a nunnery, or to death.

Enter Theseus, Hippolyta, Philostrate, and Attendants.

THESEUS   Now, fair Hippolyta, our nuptial hour
Draws on apace. Four happy days bring in
Another moon. But O, methinks, how slow
This old moon wanes.

HIPPOLYTA   Four days will quickly steep themselves in night,
Four nights will quickly dream away the time.

THESEUS   Hippolyta, I woo'd thee with my sword,
And won thy love doing thee injuries.
But I will wed thee in another key,
With pomp, with triumph, and with reveling.

Enter Egeus and his daughter Hermia, Lysander, and Demetrius.

EGEUS   Happy be Theseus, our renowned Duke.

THESEUS	Thanks, good Egeus. What's the news with thee?
EGEUS	Full of vexation come I, with complaint
	Against my child, my daughter Hermia.
	Stand forth, Demetrius. My noble lord,
	This man hath my consent to marry her.
	Stand forth, Lysander. And, my gracious Duke,
	This man hath bewitch'd my daughter's heart.
	And if she will not here before your Grace
	Consent to marry with Demetrius,
	I beg the ancient privilege of Athens —
	As she is mine, I may dispose of her,
	Which shall be either to this gentleman,
	Or to her death, according to our law.
THESEUS	What say you, Hermia? Be advis'd, fair maid.
	To you your father should be as a god.
	Demetrius is a worthy gentleman.
HERMIA	So is Lysander.
THESEUS	In himself he is,
	But in this kind, wanting your father's voice,
	The other must be held the worthier.
HERMIA	I would my father look'd but with my eyes.
THESEUS	Rather your eyes must with his judgment look.
DEMETRIUS	Relent, sweet Hermia; and, Lysander, yield.
LYSANDER	You have her father's love, Demetrius.
	Let me have Hermia's. Do you marry him.
EGEUS	Scornful Lysander, true, he hath my love,
	And what is mine my love shall render him.
LYSANDER	I am, my lord, as well deriv'd as he,
	As well possess'd. My love is more than his.
	And I am belov'd of beauteous Hermia.
	Demetrius made love to Helena
	And won her soul; and she, sweet lady, dotes
	Upon this spotted and inconstant man.
THESEUS	I must confess that I have heard so much,
	And with Demetrius thought to have spoke thereof;
	But being overfull of self-affairs,
	My mind did lose it. But, Demetrius, come,
	And come Egeus, you shall go with me.
	I have some private schooling for you both.
	For you, fair Hermia, by the next new moon,
	The sealing day betwixt my love and me,
	Fit your fancies to your father's will;
	Or else the law of Athens yields you up —
	Which by no means we may extenuate —
	To death or to a vow of single life.

Exeunt all but Lysander and Hermia.

LYSANDER   Ay me! For aught that I could ever read,
Could ever hear by tale or history,
The course of true love never did run smooth.

HERMIA   If then true lovers have been ever cross'd,
It stands as an edict in destiny,
As due to love, as thoughts, and dreams, and sighs.

LYSANDER   Hear me, Hermia. I have a widow aunt;
From Athens is her house remote seven leagues.
There, gentle Hermia, may I marry thee,
And to that place the sharp Athenian law
Cannot pursue us. If thou lov'st me, then
Steal forth thy father's house tomorrow night.
And in the wood, a league without the town,
There will I stay for thee.

HERMIA   My good Lysander,
In that same place thou hast appointed me,
Tomorrow truly will I meet with thee.

LYSANDER   Keep promise, love. Look, here comes Helena.
Enter Helena.

HERMIA   God speed, fair Helena, whither away?

HELENA   Call you me fair? That fair again unsay.
O teach me how you look, and with what art
You sway the motion of Demetrius' heart.

HERMIA   I frown upon him, yet he loves me still.

HELENA   O that your frowns would teach my smiles such skill.

HERMIA   I give him curses, yet he gives me love.

HELENA   O that my prayers could such affection move.

HERMIA   Take comfort. He no more shall see my face;
Lysander and myself will fly this place.
Tomorrow night, in the wood where you and I
Upon faint primrose beds were wont to lie,
Emptying our bosoms of their counsel sweet,
There my Lysander and myself shall meet;
And thence from Athens turn away our eyes
To seek new friends and stranger companies.
Keep word, Lysander. We must starve our sight
From lovers' food till morrow deep midnight.
Farewell, sweet playfellow.   *Exit Hermia.*

LYSANDER   Helena, adieu.
As you on him, Demetrius dote on you.

HELENA   How happy some o'er other some can be!
Through Athens I am thought as fair as she.
But what of that? Demetrius thinks not so.
He will not know what all but he do know.

I will go tell him of fair Hermia's flight.
Then to the wood will he tomorrow night
Pursue her; and for this intelligence
If I have thanks, it is a dear expense.   *Exit.*

Scene 2

*Hermia and Lysander are to meet in a wood near Athens where
they think they will be all alone in the night. But Demetrius will
be following them. And Helena will be following Demetrius.
Furthermore, the wood is the home of a host of elves and fairies.
Oberon and Titania, the King and Queen of the Fairies, are involved in a bitter family quarrel. In his anger, Oberon plans to
play a mean trick on Titania; while she is sleeping he will charm
her eyes so that she will fall madly in love with the first creature
she sees when she awakes.*

*Enter a Fairy at one door and Robin Goodfellow (Puck) at
another.*

PUCK   How now, spirit, whither wander you?
FAIRY   Over hill, over dale, through bush, through brier,
        Over park, over pale, through flood, through fire;
        I do wander every where,
        Swifter than the moon's sphere.
        I must go seek some dewdrops here,
        And hang a pearl in every cowslip's ear.
        Farewell, thou lob of spirits; I'll be gone.
        Our Queen and all her elves come here anon.
PUCK   The King doth keep his revels here tonight.
        Take heed the Queen come not within his sight.
        For Oberon is passing fell and wrath,
        Because that she, as her attendant, hath
        A lovely boy, stol'n from an Indian king.
        She never had so sweet a changeling.
        And jealous Oberon would have the child
        Knight of his train, to trace the forests wild.
FAIRY   Either I mistake your shape and making quite,
        Or else you are that shrewd and knavish sprite
        Call'd Robin Goodfellow. Are not you he,

	That frights the maidens of the villagery?
	Those that Hobgoblin call you, and sweet Puck,
	You do their work, and they shall have good luck.
	Are not you he?
PUCK	Thou speakest aright;
	I am that merry wanderer of the night.
	But room, fairy, here comes Oberon.
FAIRY	And here my mistress. Would that he were gone!

Enter Oberon, the King of the Fairies, at one door with his train, and Titania, the Queen, at another with hers.

OBERON	Ill met by moonlight, proud Titania.
TITANIA	Never, since the middle summer's spring,
	Met we on hill, in dale, forest, or mead,
	To dance our ringlets to the whistling wind,
	But with thy brawls thou hast disturb'd our sport.
	Therefore the winds, piping to us in vain,
	As in revenge, have suck'd up from the sea
	Contagious fogs. Hoary-headed frosts
	Fall in the fresh lap of the crimson rose,
	And on old Hiems' thin and icy crown
	An odorous chaplet of sweet summer buds
	Is, as in mockery, set. The seasons change
	Their wonted liveries; and the mazed world
	Now knows not which is which.
	And this same progeny of evils comes
	From our debate, from our dissension.
OBERON	Do you amend it then; it lies in you.
	I do but beg a little changeling boy,
	To be my henchman.
TITANIA	Set your heart at rest;
	The fairy land buys not the child of me.
	His mother was a vot'ress of my order.
	But she being mortal, of that boy did die,
	And for her sake do I rear up her boy,
	And for her sake I will not part with him,
	Not for thy fairy kingdom. Fairies, away.
	We shall chide downright, if I longer stay.

Exeunt Titania and Fairies.

OBERON	Well, go thy way. Thou shalt not from this grove,
	Till I torment thee for this injury.
	My gentle Puck, come hither. Thou remembrest
	I show'd thee once a little western flower
	Call'd love-in-idleness. Fetch me that flower.
	The juice of it, on sleeping eyelids laid,
	Will make or man or woman madly dote

	Upon the next live creature that it sees.
PUCK	I'll put a girdle round about the earth
	In forty minutes. *Exit.*
OBERON	Having once this juice,

PUCK
I'll put a girdle round about the earth
In forty minutes.   *Exit.*

OBERON   Having once this juice,
I'll watch Titania, when she is asleep,
And drop the liquor of it in her eyes.
The next thing then she waking looks upon,
Be it on lion, bear, or busy ape,
She shall pursue it with the soul of love.
And ere I take this charm off from her sight,
I'll make her render up her page to me.
But who comes here? I am invisible,
And I will overhear their conference.
Enter Demetrius, Helena following him.

DEMETRIUS
I love thee not, therefore pursue me not.
Where is Lysander, and fair Hermia?
Thou told'st me they were stol'n into this wood.
Hence, get thee gone, and follow me no more,
For I am sick when I do look on thee.

HELENA
And I am sick when I look not on you.

DEMETRIUS
I'll run from thee, and hide me in the brakes,
And leave thee to the mercy of wild beasts.

HELENA
The wildest hath not such a heart as you.
Run when you will.   *Exit Demetrius.*
                    The story shall be chang'd;
Apollo flies, and Daphne holds the chase.   *Exit.*

*Oberon is not all naughtiness. He feels sorry for Helena,
spurned by Demetrius, and wants to set things right for her.
When Puck returns with the magic purple flower, Oberon in-
structs him to follow Helena and Demetrius and, when they are
asleep, to place some of the magic potion on Demetrius's eyes;
when he wakes up he will find himself miraculously in love with
Helena and all will be well. Unfortunately, neither Puck nor
Oberon knows that there are two pairs of lovers in the wood.
As it turns out, Puck finds the wrong lovers and puts the charm
on the wrong eyes — Lysander's eyes — with disastrous results.*

OBERON
Fare thee well, nymph. Ere he do leave this grove,
Thou shalt fly him, and he shall seek thy love.
Enter Puck.
Hast thou the flower there? Welcome, wanderer.

PUCK
Ay, there it is.

OBERON
                    I pray thee give it me.
I know a bank where the wild thyme blows,

	Where oxlips and the nodding violet grows,

Where oxlips and the nodding violet grows,
Quite overcanopied with luscious woodbine,
With sweet musk-roses, and with eglantine.
There sleeps Titania sometime of the night,
Lull'd in these flowers with dances and delight.
And with the juice of this I'll streak her eyes,
And make her full of hateful fantasies.
Take thou some of it, and seek through this grove:
A sweet Athenian lady is in love
With a disdainful youth. Anoint his eyes,
But do it when the next thing he espies
May be the lady. Thou shalt know the man
By the Athenian garments he hath on.
And look thou meet me ere the first cock crow.

PUCK   Fear not, my lord, your servant shall do so.   *Exeunt.*

Enter Titania, with her train.

TITANIA   Come, now a roundel, and a fairy song.
Then, for the third part of a minute, hence —
Some to kill cankers in the musk-rose buds,
Some war with reremice for their leathern wings,
To make my small elves coats. Sing me asleep;
Then to your offices, and let me rest.

Fairies sing and dance.

FIRST FAIRY   You spotted snakes with double tongue,
Thorny hedgehogs be not seen,
Newts and blindworms do no wrong,
Come not near our Fairy Queen.

FAIRIES   Philomel, with melody,
Sing in our sweet lullaby,
Lulla, lulla, lullaby, lulla, lulla, lullaby;
Never harm, nor spell, nor charm,
Come our lovely lady nigh.
So good night, with lullaby.

FIRST FAIRY   Weaving spiders, come not here;
Hence, you long-legg'd spinners, hence.
Beetles black, approach not near;
Worm nor snail, do no offense.

FAIRIES   Philomel, with melody,
Sing in our sweet lullaby,
Lulla, lulla, lullaby, lulla, lulla, lullaby;
Never harm, nor spell, nor charm,
Come our lovely lady nigh.
So good night, with lullaby.

Titania sleeps.

SECOND FAIRY   Hence, away. Now all is well.

	One aloof stand sentinel. *Exeunt Fairies.*
	Enter Oberon and squeezes the flower on Titania's eyes.
OBERON	What thou seest when thou dost wake,
	Do it for thy true-love take;
	Love and languish for his sake. *Exit.*
	Enter Lysander and Hermia.
LYSANDER	Fair love, you faint with wand'ring in the wood,
	And to speak troth I have forgot our way.
	We'll rest us, Hermia, if you think it good,
	And tarry for the comfort of the day.
HERMIA	Be it so, Lysander; find you out a bed,
	For I upon this bank will rest my head.
LYSANDER	Here is my bed. Sleep give thee all his rest.
HERMIA	With half that wish the wisher's eyes be press'd.
	Hermia and Lysander sleep.
	Enter Puck.
PUCK	Through the forest have I gone,
	But Athenian found I none.
	Night and silence, who is here?
	Weeds of Athens he doth wear,
	And here the maiden, sleeping sound,
	On the dank and dirty ground.
	Squeezes the flower on Lysander's eyes.
	Churl, upon thy eyes I throw
	All the power this charm doth owe.
	So awake when I am gone;
	For I must now to Oberon. *Exit.*
	Enter Demetrius and Helena running.
HELENA	Stay, though thou kill me, sweet Demetrius.
DEMETRIUS	I charge thee hence, and do not haunt me thus. *Exit.*
HELENA	O, I am out of breath in this fond chase;
	The more my prayer, the lesser is my grace.
	But who is here? Lysander, on the ground.
	Dead, or asleep? I see no blood, no wound.
	Lysander, if you live, good sir, awake.
LYSANDER	*Awaking.* And run through fire I will for thy sweet sake.
	Where is Demetrius? O how fit a word
	Is that vile name to perish on my sword!
HELENA	Do not say so, Lysander, say not so.
	What though he love your Hermia? Lord, what though?
	Yet Hermia still loves you; then be content.
LYSANDER	Content with Hermia? No, I do repent
	The tedious minutes I with her have spent.
	Not Hermia, but Helena I love.
	Who will not change a raven for a dove?

52

HELENA	Wherefore was I to this keen mockery born?
	When at your hands did I deserve this scorn?
	Is 't not enough, is 't not enough, young man,
	That I did never, no, nor never can,
	Deserve a sweet look from Demetrius' eye,
	But you must flout my insufficiency?
	But fare you well; perforce I must confess
	I thought you lord of more true gentleness. *Exit.*
LYSANDER	She sees not Hermia. Hermia, sleep thou there,
	And never mayst thou come Lysander near.
	And all my powers address your love and might,
	To honor Helen, and to be her knight. *Exit.*

*Now, Lysander (who came to the woods intending to run away
with Hermia) is instead madly pursuing Helena, who is following Demetrius, who is looking for Hermia — who, in just a
moment, will wake up to set off in search of Lysander!*

HERMIA Help me, Lysander, help me; do thy best
To pluck this crawling serpent from my breast.
Ay me, for pity! What a dream was here!
Lysander, look how I do quake with fear.
Methought a serpent eat my heart away,
And you sat smiling at his cruel prey.
Lysander! What, remov'd? Lysander, lord!
What, out of hearing, gone? No sound, no word?
Alack where are you? Speak, an if you hear.
Speak, of all loves! I swoon almost with fear.
No? Then I well perceive you are not nigh:
Either death or you I'll find immediately.   *Exit.*

*Into this same wood come some loyal, loving subjects of the
Duke. Six stupid, stagestruck workmen from Athens choose the
wood as a suitably private place to rehearse a play they plan to
perform for their Duke on his wedding day, at night.*

Quince, who likes to imagine that he is a great poet, has written a "lamentable comedy" about a romantic young gallant named Pyramus who kills himself for love of his lady Thisby. Quince has cast his friend Nick Bottom in the part of Pyramus. Ridiculous Bottom. He has not the slightest doubt that he is the world's greatest actor; if he had his way he would play all the parts. Foolish Bottom. He loves to use words — big words, little words, all words — with no regard for meaning. In his first speech he tells Quince to "call them generally, man by man," which is, of course, a flat contradiction, and he describes a lion as a wild-fowl! Flute is the young boy in the group who will play the girl's part, in spite of his protestations that his beard is beginning to grow — Flute is very proud of that beard. Snug considers himself stupid, although as a joiner he actually does far more difficult and delicate woodwork than Quince can do, for Quince is only a carpenter. Starveling, the tailor, is a wizened little man accustomed to sitting cross-legged, bent over his sewing. Every one of these clowns is afraid of his own shadow, here in the dark woods at night. But the biggest coward of them all is Snout. He almost jumps out of his skin when Bottom demonstrates his lion's roar; then he covers up by asking "Will not the ladies be afeard of the lion?"

These characters are too much for Puck: when he finds them he cannot resist the temptation to have some fun.

Enter the Clowns: Quince, Bottom, Snug, Flute, Snout, and Starveling.

QUINCE   Here's a marvelous convenient place for our rehearsal. This green plot shall be our stage, this hawthorn brake our tiring house. Is all our company here?

BOTTOM   You were best to call them generally, man by man, according to the scrip.

QUINCE   Here is the scroll of every man's name, which is thought fit, through all Athens, to play in our interlude before the Duke and Duchess, on his wedding day at night.

BOTTOM   First, good Peter Quince, say what the play treats on.

QUINCE   Marry, our play is "The Most Lamentable Comedy, and Most Cruel Death of Pyramus and Thisby."

BOTTOM   A very good piece of work, I assure you, and a merry.

QUINCE   Answer as I call you. Nick Bottom the weaver, you are set down for Pyramus.

BOTTOM   What is Pyramus? A lover, or a tyrant?

QUINCE   A lover that kills himself, most gallant, for love.

BOTTOM   That will ask some tears in the true performing of it. If I do it, let the audience look to their eyes. Yet my chief humor is for a tyrant. I could play Ercles rarely.

> The raging rocks,
> And shivering shocks,
> Shall break the locks
>   Of prison gates,
> And Phibbus' car
> Shall shine from far,
> And make and mar
>   The foolish Fates.

This was lofty. Now name the rest of the players. This is Ercles' vein, a tyrant's vein. A lover is more condoling.

QUINCE	Francis Flute the bellows-mender.
FLUTE	Here, Peter Quince.
QUINCE	Flute, you must take Thisby on you.
FLUTE	What is Thisby? A wand'ring knight?
QUINCE	It is the lady that Pyramus must love.
FLUTE	Nay faith, let not me play a woman. I have a beard coming.
QUINCE	That's all one. You shall play it in a mask, and you may speak as small as you will.
BOTTOM	An I may hide my face, let me play Thisby too. I'll speak in a monstrous little voice: "Ah Pyramus, my lover dear, thy Thisby dear, and lady dear."
QUINCE	No no, you must play Pyramus; and, Flute, you Thisby.
BOTTOM	Well, proceed.
QUINCE	Robin Starveling the tailor.
STARVELING	Here, Peter Quince.
QUINCE	Robin Starveling, you must play Thisby's mother. Tom Snout the tinker.
SNOUT	Here, Peter Quince.
QUINCE	You, Pyramus' father; myself, Thisby's father. Snug the joiner, you the lion's part. And I hope here is a play fitted.
SNUG	Have you the lion's part written? Pray you, if it be, give it me, for I am slow of study.
QUINCE	You may do it extempore, for it is nothing but roaring.
BOTTOM	Let me play the lion too. I will roar, that I will do any man's heart good to hear me. *He roars.*
QUINCE	An you should do it too terribly, you would fright the Duchess, and the ladies, that they would shriek, and that were enough to hang us all.
BOTTOM	I will aggravate my voice so, that I will roar you as gently as any sucking dove; I will roar you an 'twere any nightingale.
SNOUT	Will not the ladies be afeard of the lion?
STARVELING	I fear it, I promise you.
BOTTOM	Masters, you ought to consider with yourselves — to bring in,

56

	God shield us, a lion among ladies is a most dreadful thing. For there is not a more fearful wild-fowl than your lion living.
STARVELING	I believe we must leave the lion out, when all is done.
BOTTOM	Not a whit. I have a device to make all well. Half his face must be seen through the lion's neck, and he himself must speak through, saying thus, or to the same defect: "Ladies," or "Fair ladies, I would wish you," or, "I would request you, not to fear. If you think I come hither as a lion, it were pity of my life. No, I am no such thing." And there indeed let him tell them plainly he is Snug the joiner.
QUINCE	Well, it shall be so. But there is two hard things: that is, to bring the moonlight into a chamber; for you know, Pyramus and Thisby meet by moonlight.
SNUG	Doth the moon shine that night we play our play?
QUINCE	Yes, it doth shine that night.
BOTTOM	Why then, the moon may shine in at the casement.
QUINCE	Ay, or else one must come in with a bush of thorns and a lant-horn, and say he comes to disfigure, or to present, the person of Moonshine. Then, there is another thing; we must have a wall in the great chamber, for Pyramus and Thisby, says the story, did talk through the chink of a wall.
SNOUT	You can never bring in a wall. What say you, Bottom?
BOTTOM	Some man or other must present Wall. And let him have some plaster, or some loam about him, to signify wall; and let him hold his fingers thus, and through that cranny shall Pyramus and Thisby whisper.
QUINCE	If that may be, then all is well. Come, Pyramus, you begin. When you have spoken your speech, enter into that brake; and so every one according to his cue.
	Enter Puck.
PUCK	What hempen homespuns have we swaggering here, So near the cradle of the Fairy Queen? What, a play toward? I'll be an auditor, An actor too perhaps, if I see cause.
QUINCE	Speak, Pyramus. Thisby, stand forth.
BOTTOM	"Thisby, the flowers of odious savors sweet —"
QUINCE	Odorous, odorous.
BOTTOM	" — odors savors sweet. So hath thy breath, my dearest Thisby dear. But hark, a voice; stay thou but here awhile, And by and by I will to thee appear." *Exit.*
PUCK	A stranger Pyramus than e'er play'd here. *Exit.*
FLUTE	Must I speak now?
QUINCE	Ay, marry, must you. For you must understand he goes but to see a noise that he heard, and is to come again.

FLUTE	"Most radiant Pyramus, most lily-white of hue,
	Of color like the red rose on triumphant brier,
	Most brisky juvenal, and eke most lovely Jew,
	As true as truest horse, that yet would never tire,
	I'll meet thee, Pyramus, at Ninny's tomb."
QUINCE	"Ninus' tomb," man. Why, you must not speak that yet; that you answer to Pyramus. You speak all your part at once, cues and all. Pyramus, enter. Your cue is past; it is "never tire."
FLUTE	O — "As true as truest horse, that yet would never tire."
	Enter Puck, and Bottom with an ass's head.
BOTTOM	If I were fair, Thisby, I were only thine.
QUINCE	O monstrous! O strange! We are haunted. Pray, masters, fly, masters! Help!
SNOUT	O Bottom, thou art chang'd. What do I see on thee?
	Exeunt all but Bottom.
BOTTOM	Why do they run away? I see their knavery. This is to make an ass of me, to fright me, if they could. But I will not stir from this place, and I will sing, that they shall hear I am not afraid.
	The woosel cock, so black of hue,
	With orange-tawny bill,
	The throstle, with his note so true,
	The wren, with little quill —
TITANIA	*Awaking.* What angel wakes me from my flowery bed?
BOTTOM	The finch, the sparrow, and the lark,
	The plainsong cuckoo gray,
	Whose note full many a man doth mark,
	And dares not answer, nay —
TITANIA	I pray thee, gentle mortal, sing again.
	Mine ear is much enamor'd of thy note;
	And thy fair virtue's force, perforce, doth move me,
	On the first view, to say, to swear, I love thee.
BOTTOM	Methinks, mistress, you should have little reason for that. And yet, to say the truth, reason and love keep little company together now-a-days.
TITANIA	Thou art as wise as thou art beautiful,
	And I do love thee; therefore, go with me.
	I'll give thee fairies to attend on thee.
	Peaseblossom, Cobweb, Moth, and Mustardseed!
	Enter four Fairies.
PEASEBLOSSOM	Ready.
COBWEB	And I.
MOTH	And I.
MUSTARDSEED	And I.
ALL FOUR	Where shall we go?
TITANIA	Be kind and courteous to this gentleman,

58

Feed him with apricocks and dewberries,
With purple grapes, green figs, and mulberries;
And pluck the wings from painted butterflies,
To fan the moonbeams from his sleeping eyes.
Nod to him, elves, and do him courtesies.

PEASEBLOSSOM   Hail, mortal!

COBWEB   Hail!

MOTH   Hail!

MUSTARDSEED   Hail!

BOTTOM   I cry your worships mercy heartily. I beseech your worship's name.

COBWEB   Cobweb.

BOTTOM   I shall desire you of more acquaintance, good Master Cobweb. If I cut my finger, I shall make bold with you. Your name, honest gentleman?

PEASEBLOSSOM   Peaseblossom.

BOTTOM   I pray you commend me to Mistress Squash, your mother, and

	to Master Peascod, your father, good Master Peaseblossom. Your name I beseech you, sir?
MUSTARDSEED	Mustardseed.
BOTTOM	Good Master Mustardseed, I know your patience well. I promise you, your kindred hath made my eyes water ere now.
TITANIA	Come, wait upon him; lead him to my bower.
	The moon, methinks, looks with a wat'ry eye,
	And when she weeps, weeps every little flower.
	Tie up my love's tongue, bring him silently. *Exeunt.*
	Enter Oberon.
OBERON	I wonder if Titania be awak'd.
	Enter Puck.
	Here comes my messenger. How now, mad spirit?
PUCK	My mistress with a monster is in love.
	Near to her close and consecrated bower,
	While she was in her dull and sleeping hour,
	A crew of patches, rude mechanicals,
	That work for bread upon Athenian stalls,
	Were met together to rehearse a play,
	Intended for great Theseus' nuptial day.
	He that was Pyramus enter'd in a brake;
	When I did him at this advantage take,
	An ass's noll I fixed on his head.
	Anon his Thisby must be answered,
	And forth my mimic comes. When they him spy,
	Away his fellows, full of fear, did fly.
	When in that moment — so it came to pass —
	Titania wak'd, and straightway lov'd an ass.
OBERON	This falls out better than I could devise.
	But hast thou yet latch'd the Athenian's eyes
	With the love-juice, as I did bid thee do?
PUCK	I took him sleeping — that is finish'd too.
	Enter Demetrius and Hermia.
OBERON	Stand close. This is the same Athenian.
PUCK	This is the woman, but not this the man.
DEMETRIUS	O why rebuke you him that loves you so?
	Lay breath so bitter on your bitter foe.
HERMIA	If thou hast slain Lysander in his sleep,
	Being o'er shoes in blood, plunge in the deep,
	And kill me too.
DEMETRIUS	You spend your passion on a mispris'd mood.
	I am not guilty of Lysander's blood.
	Nor is he dead, for aught that I can tell.
HERMIA	I pray thee, tell me then that he is well.
DEMETRIUS	And if I could, what should I get therefore?

60

HERMIA	A privilege never to see me more. *Exit.*
DEMETRIUS	There is no following her in this fierce vein.
	Here therefore for a while I will remain. *Sleeps.*

Oberon is delighted with the way his plot against Titania has turned out, but annoyed that his plan for Helena and Demetrius has gone all wrong. Instead of patching up their romance, Puck has broken up Hermia's, and, knowing what delight Puck takes in doing mischief, Oberon is not convinced that it was entirely an accident. However, all he can do now is try to mend matters as quickly as possible. Here is a perfect opportunity to charm Demetrius's eyes — just in time, too, for Helena is right on his heels. But there is no chance to take the mistaken spell off of Lysander's eyes before the four lovers meet — and what a meeting that turns out to be! Whereas Lysander and Demetrius had both come to the wood in love with Hermia, they are soon fighting over Helena — who thinks they are making fun of her, and that Hermia is in on the plot.

OBERON	What hast thou done? Thou hast mistaken quite,
	And laid the love-juice on some true-love's sight.
	About the wood, go swifter than the wind,
	And Helena of Athens look thou find.
	By some illusion see thou bring her here.
	I'll charm his eyes against she do appear.
PUCK	I go, I go, look how I go,
	Swifter than arrow from the Tartar's bow. *Exit.*
	Oberon squeezes the flower on Demetrius's eyes.
OBERON	Flower of this purple dye,
	When his love he doth espy,
	Let her shine as gloriously
	As the Venus of the sky.
	Enter Puck.
PUCK	Captain of our fairy band,
	Helena is here at hand,
	And the youth, mistook by me,
	Pleading for a lover's fee.
	Shall we their fond pageant see?
	Lord, what fools these mortals be!
	Enter Helena and Lysander.
LYSANDER	Why should you think that I should woo in scorn?
	Scorn and derision never come in tears.
	Look, when I vow, I weep; and vows so born,
	In their nativity all truth appears.
HELENA	These vows are Hermia's. Will you give her o'er?

LYSANDER	I had no judgment, when to her I swore.
DEMETRIUS	*Awaking.* O Helen, goddess, nymph, perfect, divine,
	To what, my love, shall I compare thine eyne?
	Crystal is muddy. O, how ripe in show
	Thy lips, those kissing cherries, tempting grow!
HELENA	O spite! O hell! I see you all are bent
	To set against me for your merriment.
LYSANDER	You are unkind, Demetrius; be not so,
	For you love Hermia; this you know I know.
	And here, with all good will, with all my heart,
	In Hermia's love I yield you up my part.
	And yours of Helena to me bequeath,
	Whom I do love, and will do to my death.
HELENA	Never did mockers waste more idle breath.
DEMETRIUS	Lysander, keep thy Hermia; I will none.
	If e'er I lov'd her, all that love is gone.
	My heart to her but as guest-wise sojourn'd,
	And now to Helen is it home return'd.
	Enter Hermia.
HERMIA	Dark night, that from the eye his function takes,
	The ear more quick of apprehension makes.
	Thou art not by mine eye, Lysander, found;
	Mine ear, I thank it, brought me to thy sound.
	But why unkindly didst thou leave me so?
LYSANDER	Why should he stay, whom love doth press to go?
HERMIA	What love could press Lysander from my side?
LYSANDER	Lysander's love, that would not let him bide —
	Fair Helena, who more engilds the night
	Than all yon fiery oes and eyes of light.
HERMIA	You speak not as you think; it cannot be.
HELENA	Lo, she is one of this confederacy.
	Now I perceive they have conjoin'd all three,
	To fashion this false sport in spite of me.
HERMIA	I am amazed at your passionate words.
HELENA	Have you not set Lysander, as in scorn,
	To follow me, and praise my eyes and face?
	And made your other love, Demetrius,
	To call me goddess, nymph, divine, and rare?
HERMIA	I understand not what you mean by this.
HELENA	Ay, do, persever, counterfeit sad looks;
	Wink each at other when I turn my back.
LYSANDER	Helen, I love thee, by my life I do.
DEMETRIUS	I say I love thee more than he can do.
HELENA	O excellent!
HERMIA	Sweet, do not scorn her so.

LYSANDER	*To Hermia.* Hang off, thou cat, thou burr! Vile thing, let loose.
HERMIA	Do you not jest?
HELENA	Yes, sooth, and so do you.
HERMIA	Am not I Hermia? Are not you Lysander?
	Since night you lov'd me; yet since night you left me.
	Why then, you left me — O, the gods forbid —
	In earnest, shall I say?
LYSANDER	Ay, by my life.
	Be certain, nothing truer; 'tis no jest
	That I do hate thee, and love Helena.
HERMIA	*To Helena.* O me, you juggler, you cankerblossom,
	You thief of love. What, have you come by night,
	And stol'n my love's heart from him?
HELENA	Fine, i' faith!
	Fie, fie, you counterfeit, you puppet, you.
HERMIA	Puppet? Why so? Ay, that way goes the game.
	Now I perceive that she hath made compare
	Between our statures. I am not yet so low,
	But that my nails can reach unto thine eyes.
HELENA	I pray you, though you mock me, gentlemen,
	Let her not hurt me.
LYSANDER	She shall not harm thee, Helena.
DEMETRIUS	No, sir, she shall not, though you take her part.
HELENA	O, when she's angry, she is keen and shrewd.
	And though she be but little, she is fierce.
HERMIA	"Little" again? Nothing but "low" and "little"!
	Why will you suffer her to flout me thus?
	Let me come to her.
LYSANDER	Get you gone, you dwarf,
	You bead, you acorn.
DEMETRIUS	You are too officious
	In her behalf that scorns your services.
LYSANDER	Now follow, if thou dar'st, to try whose right,
	Or thine or mine, is most in Helena.
DEMETRIUS	Follow? Nay, I'll go with thee, cheek by jowl.
	Exeunt Lysander and Demetrius.
HERMIA	You, mistress, all this coil is long of you.
	Nay, go not back.
HELENA	I will not trust you, I,
	Nor longer stay in your curst company.
	Your hands than mine are quicker for a fray.
	My legs are longer though, to run away.
	Exeunt Helena and Hermia.
OBERON	This is thy negligence. Still thou mistak'st,
	Or else commit'st thy knaveries wilfully.

PUCK	Believe me, King of Shadows, I mistook.
	Did not you tell me I should know the man
	By the Athenian garments he had on?
	And so far blameless proves my enterprise
	That I have 'nointed an Athenian's eyes;
	And so far am I glad it so did sort,
	As this their jangling I esteem a sport.
OBERON	Thou seest these lovers seek a place to fight.
	Hie therefore, Robin, overcast the night,
	And lead these testy rivals so astray,
	As one come not within another's way,
	Till o'er their brows death-counterfeiting sleep
	With leaden legs and batty wings doth creep.
	Then crush this herb into Lysander's eye,
	Whose liquor hath this virtuous property,
	When they next wake, all this derision
	Shall seem a dream and fruitless vision.
	Whiles I in this affair do thee employ,
	I'll to my Queen and beg her Indian boy;
	And then I will her charmed eye release
	From monster's view, and all things shall be peace.
PUCK	My fairy lord, this must be done with haste,
	For night's swift dragons cut the clouds full fast,
	And yonder shines Aurora's harbinger;
	At whose approach, ghosts, wand'ring here and there,
	Troop home to churchyards.
OBERON	Haste, make no delay.
	We may effect this business yet ere day. *Exit.*

The threads of the plot are tightly tangled now, and dawn will soon be breaking. With luck, however, Oberon and Puck will get everything straight in time. Lysander and Demetrius will be prevented from killing each other; the spell will be removed from Lysander's eyes and he will once again love Hermia; Demetrius will discover that Helena is the girl he truly loves; Titania will give Oberon her changeling child and harmony will be restored in the fairies' royal family; and Hermia will be saved from death.

PUCK	Up and down, up and down,
	I will lead them up and down.
	Here comes one.
	Enter Lysander.
LYSANDER	Where art thou, proud Demetrius? Speak thou now.
PUCK	*Mimicking Demetrius's voice.*
	Here, villain, drawn and ready. Where art thou?
LYSANDER	I will be with thee straight.
PUCK	Follow me then
	To plainer ground. *Exit Lysander.*
	Enter Demetrius.
DEMETRIUS	Lysander, speak again.
	Thou runaway, thou coward, art thou fled?
	Speak! In some bush? Where dost thou hide thy head?
PUCK	*In Lysander's voice.* Thou coward, art thou bragging to the stars,
	Telling the bushes that thou look'st for wars,
	And wilt not come?
DEMETRIUS	Recreant, art thou there?
PUCK	Follow my voice; we'll try no manhood here. *Exeunt.*
	Enter Lysander.
LYSANDER	He goes before me, and still dares me on.
	When I come where he calls, then he is gone.
	Now fallen am I in dark uneven way,
	And here will rest me. Come, thou gentle day,
	For if but once thou show me thy gray light,
	I'll find Demetrius, and revenge this spite. *Sleeps.*
	Enter Puck followed by Demetrius.
DEMETRIUS	Where art thou now?
PUCK	*In Lysander's voice.* Come hither. I am here.
DEMETRIUS	Nay then thou mock'st me. Thou shalt buy this dear,
	If ever I thy face by daylight see.
	Now, go thy way. Faintness constraineth me
	To measure out my length on this cold bed.
	By day's approach look to be visited. *Sleeps.*
	Enter Helena.
HELENA	O weary night, O long and tedious night,
	Abate thy hours. Shine comforts from the east,
	That I may back to Athens by daylight,
	From these that my poor company detest;
	And sleep, that sometimes shuts up sorrow's eye,
	Steal me awhile from mine own company. *Sleeps.*
PUCK	Yet but three? Come one more.
	Two of both kinds makes up four.
	Here she comes, curst and sad.

	Cupid is a knavish lad,
	Thus to make poor females mad.
	Enter Hermia.
HERMIA	Never so weary, never so in woe,
	Bedabbled with the dew, and torn with briers,
	I can no further crawl, no further go.
	My legs can keep no pace with my desires.
	Here will I rest me till the break of day.
	Heavens shield Lysander, if they mean a fray. *Sleeps.*
PUCK	On the ground, sleep sound.
	I'll apply to your eye,
	Gentle lover, remedy.
	He squeezes the herb on Lysander's eyes.
	When thou wak'st, thou tak'st
	True delight in the sight
	Of thy former lady's eye.
	And the country proverb known,
	That every man should take his own,
	In your waking shall be shown.
	Jack shall have Jill; naught shall go ill;
	The man shall have his mare again,
	And all shall be well. *Exit.*
	Enter Titania, Bottom, and Fairies; Oberon behind unseen.
TITANIA	Come, sit thee down upon this flow'ry bed,
	While I thy amiable cheeks do coy,
	And stick musk-roses in thy sleek smooth head,
	And kiss thy fair large ears, my gentle joy.
BOTTOM	Where's Peaseblossom?
PEASEBLOSSOM	Ready.
BOTTOM	Scratch my head, Peaseblossom. Where's Mounsieur Cobweb?
COBWEB	Ready.
BOTTOM	Good mounsieur, get you your weapons in your hand, and kill me a red-hipped humble-bee; and bring me the honeybag. Where's Mounsieur Mustardseed?
MUSTARDSEED	What's your will?
BOTTOM	Nothing, good mounsieur, but to help Cavalery Peaseblossom to scratch. I must to the barber's, mounsieur, for methinks I am marvelous hairy about the face. And I am such a tender ass, if my hair do but tickle me, I must scratch.
TITANIA	Say, sweet love, what thou desirest to eat.
BOTTOM	Truly, methinks I have a great desire to a bottle of hay. Good hay, sweet hay, hath no fellow. But, I pray you, let none of your people stir me. I have an exposition of sleep come upon me.
TITANIA	Sleep thou, and I will wind thee in my arms.

Fairies, be gone. *Exeunt Fairies.*
                        So doth the woodbine
Gently entwist; the female ivy so
Enrings the barky fingers of the elm.
O how I love thee! How I dote on thee!
Titania and Bottom sleep.
Enter Puck.

OBERON   Welcome, good Robin. Seest thou this sweet sight?
Her dotage now I do begin to pity.
For meeting her of late, behind the wood,
Seeking sweet favors for this hateful fool,
I then did ask of her her changeling child,
Which straight she gave me. I will undo
This hateful imperfection of her eyes.
He touches her eyes with an herb.
    Be as thou wast wont to be;
    See as thou wast wont to see.
Now, my Titania, wake you, my sweet Queen.

TITANIA   My Oberon, what visions have I seen!
Methought I was enamor'd of an ass.

OBERON   There lies your love.

TITANIA   How came these things to pass?

OBERON   Silence awhile. Robin, take off this head.
Sound, music! Come, my Queen, take hands with me,
And rock the ground whereon these sleepers be.
The Fairies dance.

PUCK   Fairy King, attend, and mark,
I do hear the morning lark.

OBERON   Then, my Queen, in silence sad,
Trip we after night's shade.

TITANIA   Come, my lord, and in our flight,
Tell me how it came this night
That I sleeping here was found,
With these mortals on the ground. *Exeunt.*

*Now the night is gone and day is breaking. But how, in a
theater without lighting equipment, does one show the coming
of dawn? Shakespeare always has his characters tell the audience whether it is night or day. But here he accomplishes
something much more difficult: he shows the gradual approach
of day. The first hint of dawn was in Puck's speech on page 64:*
    "For night's swift dragons cut the clouds full fast,
    And yonder shines Aurora's harbinger."
A little later Puck gave a more urgent warning:
    "Fairy King, attend, and mark,

I do hear the morning lark."

With that the fairies were gone, "following darkness like a dream." Now the break of day is heralded by the sound of the Duke's hunting horns. With that sound it is almost possible to see the sun burst over the horizon. Soon it will be broad day.

Horns winded. Enter Theseus, Hippolyta, Egeus, and Attendants.

THESEUS Go, one of you, find out the forester;
For since we have the vaward of the day,
My love shall hear the music of my hounds.
We will, fair Queen, up to the mountain's top,
And mark the musical confusion
Of hounds and echo in conjunction.

HIPPOLYTA I was with Hercules and Cadmus once,
When in a wood of Crete they bay'd the bear
With hounds of Sparta; never did I hear
So musical a discord, such sweet thunder.

THESEUS My hounds are bred out of the Spartan kind,
Slow in pursuit, but match'd in mouth like bells,
Each under each. But soft, what nymphs are these?

EGEUS My lord, this is my daughter here asleep,
And this Lysander; this Demetrius is,
This Helena, old Nedar's Helena.
I wonder of their being here together.

THESEUS No doubt they rose up early to observe
The rite of May. Go and bid the huntsmen
Wake them with their horns.
Horns within. Demetrius, Lysander, Hermia, and Helena all start up.

THESEUS   Good morrow, friends.

LYSANDER Pardon, my lord.

THESEUS   I pray you all, stand up.
I know you two are rival enemies.
How comes this gentle concord in the world?

LYSANDER My lord, I shall reply amazedly,
Half sleep, half waking, but truly, as I think.
I came with Hermia hither. Our intent
Was to be gone from Athens, where we might,
Without the peril of Athenian law —

EGEUS Enough, enough, my lord. You have enough.
I beg the law, the law, upon his head.

DEMETRIUS My lord, fair Helen told me of their stealth,
And I in fury hither follow'd them,
Fair Helena in fancy following me.

	But, my good lord, I wot not by what power —
	But by some power it is — my love to Hermia
	Melted as the snow, and now my love
	Is only Helena. To her, my lord,
	Was I betroth'd ere I saw Hermia.
THESEUS	Fair lovers, you are fortunately met.
	Egeus, I will overbear your will;
	For in the temple, by and by, with us
	These couples shall eternally be knit.
	And, for the morning now is something worn,
	Our purpos'd hunting shall be set aside.
	Away with us to Athens. Three and three,
	We'll hold a feast in great solemnity.

Exeunt Theseus, Hippolyta, Egeus, and Attendants.

DEMETRIUS	These things seem small and indistinguishable,
	Like far-off mountains turned into clouds.
HERMIA	Methinks I see these things with parted eye,
	When every thing seems double.
HELENA	So methinks.
	And I have found Demetrius, like a jewel,
	Mine own, and not mine own.
DEMETRIUS	It seems to me
	That yet we sleep, we dream. Do not you think
	The Duke was here, and bid us follow him?
HERMIA	Yea, and my father.
HELENA	And Hippolyta.
LYSANDER	And he did bid us follow to the temple.
DEMETRIUS	Why then we are awake; let's follow him,
	And by the way let us recount our dreams. *Exeunt.*
BOTTOM	*Awaking.* When my cue comes, call me, and I will answer. My next is, "Most fair Pyramus." Hey-ho. Peter Quince? Flute the bellows-mender? Snout the tinker? Starveling? God's my life! Stol'n hence, and left me asleep? I have had a dream, past the wit of man to say what dream it was. Man is but an ass, if he go about to expound this dream. Methought I was, and methought I had — but man is but a patch'd fool, if he will offer to say what methought I had. The eye of man hath not heard, the ear of man hath not seen, man's hand is not able to taste, his tongue to conceive, nor his heart to report, what my dream was. I will get Peter Quince to write a ballad of this dream, and I will sing it in the latter end of our play, before the Duke. *Exit.*

Scene 3

The play ends in a merry scene at the Duke's palace. The three pairs of lovers are now married. To the great amusement of the happy couples, Bottom and his friends present their hilarious tragedy. Quince has written some of the worst poetry ever heard. His use of poetic devices goes to ridiculous extremes. Notice his extravagant use of alliteration, for example:

> "Whereat, with blade, with bloody blameful blade,
> He bravely broach'd his boiling bloody breast."

And when he speaks his poetry, Quince pays no attention to meaning. He sails blithely past periods or comes to a complete stop in the middle of a sentence, and ends with nonsense like "All for your delight, we are not here." Bottom overacts unforgivably. Starveling has stagefright so badly he forgets his lines. All in all, worse actors could hardly be imagined. During the play members of the wedding party whisper witty comments to each other.

	Enter Theseus, Hippolyta, Egeus, Philostrate, and Attendants.
HIPPOLYTA	'Tis strange, my Theseus, that these lovers speak of.
THESEUS	More strange than true. I never may believe
	These antic fables, nor these fairy toys.
	The lunatic, the lover, and the poet
	Are of imagination all compact.
HIPPOLYTA	Here come the lovers, full of joy and mirth.
	Enter Lysander, Demetrius, Hermia, and Helena.
THESEUS	Joy, gentle friends, joy and fresh days of love
	Accompany your hearts.
LYSANDER	More than to us
	Wait in your royal walks, your board, your bed.
THESEUS	Come now; what masques, what dances shall we have,
	To wear away this long age of three hours,
	Between our after-supper and bedtime?
PHILOSTRATE	There is a brief, how many sports are ripe.
THESEUS	"The thrice three Muses, mourning for the death
	Of Learning, late deceas'd in beggary."
	That is some satire keen and critical,
	Not sorting with a nuptial ceremony.
	"A tedious brief scene of young Pyramus

	And his love Thisby; very tragical mirth."
	Merry and tragical? Tedious and brief?
	How shall we find the concord of this discord?
	What are they that do play it?
PHILOSTRATE	Hard-handed men, that work in Athens here,
	Which never labor'd in their minds till now.
THESEUS	And we will hear it.
PHILOSTRATE	No, my noble lord,
	It is not for you. I have heard it over,
	And it is nothing, nothing in the world;
	Unless you can find sport in their intents.
THESEUS	Never any thing can be amiss,
	When simpleness and duty tender it.
	Go bring them in, and take your places, ladies.
PHILOSTRATE	So please your Grace, the Prologue is address'd.
THESEUS	Let him approach.
	Flourish of trumpets. Enter Quince as Prologue.
PROLOGUE	If we offend, it is with our good will.
	That you should think, we come not to offend,
	But with good will. To show our simple skill,
	That is the true beginning of our end.
	Consider then, we come but in despite.
	We do not come, as minding to content you,
	Our true intent is. All for your delight,
	We are not here. That you should here repent you,
	The actors are at hand; and, by their show,
	You shall know all, that you are like to know.
HIPPOLYTA	He hath play'd on his prologue, like a child on a recorder, a sound, but not in government.
	Enter Bottom as Pyramus, Flute as Thisby, Snout as Wall, Starveling as Moonshine, and Snug as Lion.
PROLOGUE	Gentles, perchance you wonder at this show,
	But, wonder on, till truth make all things plain.
	This man is Pyramus, if you would know;
	This beauteous lady Thisby is certain.
	This man, with lime and rough-cast, doth present
	Wall, that vile wall, which did these lovers sunder:
	And through Wall's chink, poor souls, they are content
	To whisper. At the which, let no man wonder.
	This man, with lanthorn, dog, and bush of thorn,
	Presenteth Moonshine. For if you will know,
	By moonshine did these lovers think no scorn
	To meet at Ninus' tomb, there, there to woo.
	This grisly beast, which Lion hight by name,
	The trusty Thisby, coming first by night,

Did scare away, or rather did affright.
And as she fled, her mantle she did fall.
Which Lion vile with bloody mouth did stain.
Anon comes Pyramus, sweet youth, and tall,
And finds his trusty Thisby's mantle slain.
Whereat, with blade, with bloody blameful blade,
He bravely broach'd his boiling bloody breast.
And Thisby, tarrying in mulberry shade,
His dagger drew, and died. For all the rest,
Let Lion, Moonshine, Wall, and lovers twain,
At large discourse, while here they do remain.

Exeunt Thisby, Lion, and Moonshine.

THESEUS   I wonder if the lion be to speak.
DEMETRIUS   No wonder, my lord. One lion may, when many asses do.
WALL   In this same interlude it doth befall,
             That I, one Snout by name, present a wall.
             And such a wall, as I would have you think,

	That had in it a crannied hole or chink:
	Through which the lovers, Pyramus and Thisby,
	Did whisper often, very secretly.
	This loam, this rough-cast, and this stone doth show,
	That I am that same wall; the truth is so.
	And this the cranny is, right and sinister,
	Through which the fearful lovers are to whisper.
PYRAMUS	O grim-look'd night, O night, with hue so black,
	O night, which ever art, when day is not!
	O night, O night, alack, alack, alack,
	I fear my Thisby's promise is forgot.
	And thou, O wall, O sweet, O lovely wall,
	That stand'st between her father's ground and mine,
	Thou wall, O wall, O sweet and lovely wall,
	Show me thy chink, to blink through, with mine eyne.
	Thanks, courteous wall. Jove shield thee well for this.
	But what see I? No Thisby do I sec.
	O wicked wall, through whom I see no bliss,
	Curst be thy stones, for thus deceiving me!
THESEUS	The wall methinks, being sensible, should curse again.
BOTTOM	No in truth, sir, he should not. "Deceiving me" is Thisby's cue;
	she is to enter now, and I am to spy her through the wall. You
	shall see. Yonder she comes.
	Enter Thisby.
THISBY	O wall, full often hast thou heard my moans,
	For parting my fair Pyramus, and me.
	My cherry lips have often kiss'd thy stones,
	Thy stones with lime and hair knit up in thee.
PYRAMUS	I see a voice; now will I to the chink,
	To spy an I can hear my Thisby's face.
	Thisby?
THISBY	My love thou art, my love I think.
PYRAMUS	Think what thou wilt, I am thy lover's grace.
	O kiss me, through the hole of this vile wall.
THISBY	I kiss the wall's hole, not your lips at all.
PYRAMUS	Wilt thou at Ninny's tomb meet me straightway?
THISBY	'Tide life, 'tide death, I come without delay.
	Exeunt Pyramus and Thisby.
WALL	Thus have I, Wall, my part discharged so;
	And, being done, thus Wall away doth go. *Exit.*
HIPPOLYTA	This is the silliest stuff that ever I heard.
THESEUS	The best of this kind are but shadows; and the worst are no
	worse, if imagination amend them.
HIPPOLYTA	It must be your imagination then, and not theirs.
	Enter Lion and Moonshine.

LION	You ladies, you, whose gentle hearts do fear
	The smallest monstrous mouse that creeps on floor,
	May now perchance both quake and tremble here,
	When lion rough in wildest rage doth roar.
	Then know that I one Snug the joiner am
	A lion fell, nor else no lion's dam.
	For if I should as lion come in strife
	Into this place, 'twere pity on my life.
MOONSHINE	This lanthorn doth the horned moon present —
	This lanthorn doth the horned moon present,
	Myself, the man i' th' moon do seem to be.
THESEUS	The man should be put into the lanthorn. How is it else the man i' th' moon?
DEMETRIUS	He dares not come there for the candle.
LYSANDER	Proceed, Moon.
MOONSHINE	All that I have to say, is to tell you that the lanthorn is the moon, I the man i' th' moon, this thornbush my thornbush, and this dog my dog.
	Enter Thisby.
DEMETRIUS	Here comes Thisby.
THISBY	This is old Ninny's tomb. Where is my love?
LION	*Roars.* Oh —!
	Thisby throws down her mantle and runs off.
DEMETRIUS	Well roared, Lion.
THESEUS	Well run, Thisby.
HIPPOLYTA	Well shone, Moon.
	The Lion tears Thisby's mantle, and exit.
LYSANDER	And so the lion vanish'd.
	Enter Pyramus.
DEMETRIUS	And then came Pyramus.
PYRAMUS	Sweet moon, I thank thee for thy sunny beams.
	I thank thee, moon, for shining now so bright.
	For by thy gracious, golden, glittering beams,
	I trust to take of truest Thisby sight.
	But stay. O spite! But mark, poor knight,
	What dreadful dole is here?
	Eyes do you see! How can it be!
	O dainty duck, O dear!
	Thy mantle good, what, stain'd with blood?
	Approach, ye Furies fell.
	O Fates, come, come, cut thread and thrum,
	Quail, crush, conclude, and quell.
THESEUS	This passion, and the death of a dear friend, would go near to make a man look sad.
PYRAMUS	O, wherefore, Nature, didst thou lions frame?

74

Since lion vile hath here deflower'd my dear.
Which is — no, no — which was the fairest dame
That liv'd, that lov'd, that lik'd, that look'd with cheer.
Come tears, confound. Out sword, and wound
The pap of Pyramus.
Ay, that left pap, where heart doth hop.
Thus die I, thus, thus, thus. *Stabs himself.*
Now am I dead, now am I fled,
My soul is in the sky.
Tongue lose thy light, moon take thy flight.   *Exit Moonshine.*
Now die, die, die, die, die. *Dies.*

HIPPOLYTA	How chance Moonshine is gone before Thisby comes back and finds her lover?
THESEUS	She will find him by starlight. Here she comes, and her passion ends the play.

Enter Thisby.

HIPPOLYTA	I hope she will be brief.
THISBY	Asleep my love? What, dead my dove?

O Pyramus, arise.
Speak, speak. Quite dumb? Dead, dead? A tomb
Must cover thy sweet eyes.
These lily lips, this cherry nose,
These yellow cowslip cheeks
Are gone, are gone. Lovers make moan.
His eyes were green as leeks.
O Sisters Three, come, come to me,
With hands as pale as milk;
Lay them in gore, since you have shore
With shears, his thread of silk.
Tongue, not a word. Come trusty sword;
Come blade, my breast imbrue. *Stabs herself.*
And farewell friends. Thus Thisby ends.
Adieu, adieu, adieu. *Dies.*

THESEUS	Moonshine and Lion are left to bury the dead.
DEMETRIUS	Ay, and Wall too.
BOTTOM	*Starting up.* No, I assure you, the wall is down that parted their fathers. Will it please you to see the epilogue, or to hear a Bergomask dance, between two of our company?
THESEUS	No epilogue, I pray you; for your play needs no excuse. Never excuse; for when the players are all dead, there need none to be blamed. But come, your Bergomask.

In Shakespeare's time it was the custom for every theatrical per-formance to close with a dance. The audience expected it, and the actors always provided it, even after tragedies. Whenever possible Shakespeare made the dance a part of the play itself, and in this play he gives double measure. Here the clowns dance a Bergomask, a rustic peasant dance from Bergamo, Italy; the dance was very lively, with much stamping, clapping, and finger-snapping. It is easy to imagine members of the court joining in the dancing and general merriment until late into the night.

THESEUS The iron tongue of midnight hath told twelve.
Lovers, to bed, 'tis almost fairy time.
This palpable gross play hath well beguil'd
The heavy gait of night. Sweet friends, to bed.
A fortnight hold we this solemnity,
In nightly revels, and new jollity.   *Exeunt.*

Now that the fun is over and the lovers are asleep, it is fairy time again. Through the darkened palace trip the fairies, blessing all therein, and leaving behind the faintest hint of a suspicion that it may all have been only a dream.

Enter Puck.
PUCK Now the hungry lion roars,
And the wolf behowls the moon;
Whilst the heavy ploughman snores,
All with weary task fordone.
Now it is the time of night,
That the graves, all gaping wide,
Every one lets forth his sprite,
In the church-way paths to glide.
And we fairies, that do run,
By the triple Hecate's team,
From the presence of the sun,
Following darkness like a dream,
Now are frolic; not a mouse
Shall disturb this hallow'd house.
Enter Oberon and Titania, with all their train.
OBERON Through the house give glimmering light,
By the dead and drowsy fire;
Every elf and fairy sprite,
Hop as light as bird from brier.

TITANIA	Hand in hand, with fairy grace,
	Will we sing, and bless this place.
	Fairies dance and sing.
FAIRIES	Roses, their sharp spines being gone,
	Not royal in their smell alone
	But in their hue;
	Maiden pinks, of odor faint,
	Daisies smell-less, yet most quaint,
	And sweet thyme true;
	All dear Nature's children sweet,
	Lie 'fore bride and bridegroom's feet,
	Blessing their sense.
	Not an angel of the air,
	Bird melodious or bird fair,
	Be absent hence.
OBERON	Now, until the break of day,
	Through this house each fairy stray,
	And each several chamber bless,
	Through this palace, with sweet peace.
	Trip away, make no stay;
	Meet me all by break of day. *Exeunt all but Puck.*
PUCK	If we shadows have offended,
	Think but this, and all is mended,
	That you have but slumber'd here,
	While these visions did appear.
	Give me your hands, if we be friends,
	And Robin shall restore amends. *Exit.*

The song that the fairies sang in this last scene is not really a part of the text of this play. It seems that a song was lost between the time the play was written and when it was first printed. The fairies obviously sing a song, because Titania says they will. Therefore, some Shakespearean scholars have argued that Oberon's last speech is supposed to be sung. Yet there are many reasons for questioning such an assumption. One scholar, Harley Granville-Barker, suggests that the song given here be substituted for the missing one. The words are certainly fitting for a wedding celebration and they may even have been written by Shakespeare; the song comes from The Two Noble Kinsmen, *a play almost surely written in part by Shakespeare. By an appropriate coincidence the song is sung in that play in honor of the wedding of Theseus and Hippolyta.*

3

The Comedy of Errors

Gifts from Italy

3

DURING the fifteenth and sixteenth centuries people all over Europe were entertained by groups of actors and minstrels who traveled about the country clowning, singing, dancing, and performing short plays. In Italy the actors were especially skillful. They developed a style all their own, known as *commedia dell'arte*. In the *commedia* the actors did not memorize and perform plays that had been written by someone else; they got up in front of an audience and created their comedies themselves as they went along, with only an outline of the plot as a guide. It was lively and witty, full of pantomime and acrobatics.

The actors wore masks to represent stock characters, with costumes, gestures, and even dialects that were always the same; and there was one standard setting for all the comedies, a city street or square. Among the characters there were always clowns: stupid-cunning servants called *zanni* (from *zanni* comes the English word "zany," which gives some idea what they were like). The best known of the *zanni* was Arlecchino (Harlequin), a wily fellow in a diamond-checked suit. Columbino was a saucy, mischievous servant girl. There was a pair of romantic young lovers — Pierrot and Pierrette are later, French versions of the lovers. There was a rich, greedy merchant called Pantalone, whom everybody tried to take advantage of. The Dottore was a quack doctor or professor, who went around pompously spouting Latin. The Capitano was a soldier, of course, the biggest braggart — and the biggest coward — imaginable. And then there was Pulcinella, a mean, hook-nosed old man. During the four hundred years since then, Pulcinella has turned into Punch; the familiar Punch and Judy puppet shows are modern descendants of the *commedia dell'arte*.

By Shakespeare's time the *commedia* was at its height and was being brought off the streets into the magnificent courts of the Italian noblemen. Travelers from all over Europe saw performances and took home glowing accounts; an English ambassador made an official report on it to Queen Elizabeth. It was not long before the *commedia's* influence was being seen in the plays written for the London stages, where another influence from Italy was already at work.

In those days, when a young man completed his university education, he was very likely to find himself with an excellent background in classical Latin literature, the ability to turn a fine literary phrase, a taste for Latin comedy and tragedy, and absolutely no preparation for earning a living. The flourishing theaters had a ravenous appetite for new plays, however, so many university graduates turned to writing. They patterned the plays they wrote on the plays they had studied in school, plays that had been written in Italy more than 1500 years before.

It is strange that the most important literary influence should be so old. We must look back into history a little to see why this was so.

Up until the sixteenth century the highest point in Western civilization had been reached in ancient Rome. At the height of Rome's glory there was wealth enough and leisure enough for lavish entertainment. The theater flourished. The golden age of Latin comedy was around 200 B.C. when the Roman Republic was robust and healthy, in the mood for light, gay entertainment. The two outstanding comic writers of the time were named Plautus and Terence.

During the two centuries after Plautus and Terence, Rome ceased to be a Republic and came to be ruled by Emperors who claimed descent from the Gods. The mood in Rome gradually changed. By the time of Nero, who was Emperor from A.D. 54 to A.D. 68, the most popular entertainment was the bloody combat of gladiators, and the most popular kind of drama was tragedy. The greatest writer of tragedies was Nero's former tutor, Seneca, whose plays were as cruel and bloody as his times.

With the invasions of the barbaric hordes from the north and east during the fourth and fifth centuries, the Roman Empire fell apart. The great civilization the Romans had built up came to an end, and for hundreds of years no comparable civilization developed to take its place. The great literature of Greece and Rome was forgotten.

Then came the Renaissance. The human spirit awakened from its sleep of the Dark Ages. Men rediscovered the wisdom, the knowledge, and the literature of classical Greece and Rome. They set out to explore and conquer new worlds in science, in geography, in literature.

University students in England read, admired, and performed the classical Latin comedies of Plautus and Terence and the classical Latin tragedies of Seneca, which seemed almost contemporary, since they had been rediscovered only a relatively short time before. In addition, they read, admired, and performed recent Italian copies of the classics. Naturally, therefore, when they started writing for the theaters they wrote "classical" plays of their own, and they obeyed all the classical rules for good plays.

The most important of the classical rules is that a good play must observe three unities: unity of time, unity of place, and unity of action. This meant that a play must be either a tragedy or a comedy but not a mixture (unity of action), and that everything must occur within a single day (unity of time), and all at the same place (unity of place). The setting was always a city street with several houses, an inn, and a church opening on to it, a setting that had been adopted by the *commedia dell'arte*. In addition, a play had to have five acts, and it had to be written in poetry, with long, elegant speeches full of grand-sounding words.

This last rule was the easiest of all to follow. Elizabethans loved words, loved to hear them and speak them. Words were wonderful, magical, shimmering things with hazy outlines. They were like quicksilver. If you thought you had one caught, pinned down, hemmed in, defined, suddenly it had slipped through your fingers and was off again. For there were no dictionaries then, nothing to say that such-and-such is what this word means to most people. That fact made for great freedom — and, no doubt, for great misunderstanding. But for poets it was paradise. They played with the meanings of words, and they played with the sounds of words, and they strung words together in magnificent rolling sentences.

Shakespeare was an actor. When he decided to write plays of his own, he already knew the kinds of things audiences liked and disliked. He tried his hand at every kind of play that was popular. He was immediately successful with one of his first efforts, a rousing series of history plays about King Henry VI, full of wonderfully dramatic speeches and lots of action, battle scenes with real sword-fighting and soldiers leaping from upper levels of the stage. After that he wrote an elegant artificial romance, and a classical Senecan tragedy with horror piled on horror. The fourth kind of play was, of course, a classical Roman comedy.

In *The Comedy of Errors* Shakespeare followed very closely a play by Plautus called the *Menaechmi*. In constructing his play Shakespeare was true to the classical rules for comedy, but he was true to them in his own special way. He wrote a play that was pure comedy, but added a hint of possible tragedy to heighten the tension. He wrote a play in which everything happens in a single day, yet he filled in the background with a story about happenings of twenty-five years before. And he wrote a play in which all the action can take place outside the various houses on a city square, although it does not have to; some scenes could easily be played indoors, and may very well have been. After *The Comedy of Errors* Shakespeare never again bothered about the unities. They were far too restricting; his imagination leaped through time and space in seven-league boots. Not until *The Tempest*, almost the last play he ever wrote, did he return to the unities, but in that play it happened that they served his purpose.

In *The Comedy of Errors* Shakespeare made several important additions to what Plautus had written. He doubled the confusion, and the merriment, by creating two sets of twins instead of one; he complicated the relation between husband and wife by adding the wife's sister for the second twin to fall in love with; he added a riot of puns; and he touched the whole with a little of the gay boisterous mood of the *commedia dell'arte*.

The Comedy of Errors

3

The Characters:

SOLINUS, Duke of Ephesus

AEGEON, a merchant of Syracuse

ANTIPHOLUS OF EPHESUS }
ANTIPHOLUS OF SYRACUSE } twin brothers, and sons to Aegeon and Aemilia

DROMIO OF EPHESUS }
DROMIO OF SYRACUSE } twin brothers, and bondmen to the two Antipholuses

BALTHAZAR, a merchant

ANGELO, a goldsmith

A MERCHANT, to whom Angelo is in debt

DOCTOR PINCH, a schoolmaster and conjurer

AEMILIA, an Abbess at Ephesus, wife to Aegeon

ADRIANA, wife to Antipholus of Ephesus

LUCIANA, sister to Adriana

GAOLER

OFFICER

MESSENGER

ATTENDANTS AND CITIZENS

The Scene: Ephesus

Prologue

Aegeon, a merchant from Syracuse, has come to the city of Ephesus seeking his long-lost son. Because Ephesus and Syracuse are involved in a bitter feud, Aegeon is arrested and con-

demned to die unless he can raise a ransom of a thousand marks by sundown. The Duke is curious to know what could have been important enough to bring Aegeon to this unfriendly city, and the old man tells a long, sad story.

He was once prosperous and happy, the husband of a lovely wife and father of twin sons, born while he and his wife were on a business trip to another city. He even had the very good fortune to find a second set of twin boys to bring up as servants for his sons. On the voyage home, however, their ship sank in a terrible storm. Aegeon and Aemilia, his wife, each took one son and one of the other twins. They bound the babies and themselves to a spare mast, three at each end, to save themselves from drowning. Unfortunately, the mast was dashed against a rock and broken in two. The two halves drifted apart. Aemilia was rescued by one ship and Aegeon by another. Thus they were separated and never saw each other again.

In memory of the lost boys Aegeon changed his remaining son's name to Antipholus, the name of his lost brother, and the servant twin took his brother's name, Dromio. When Antipholus was eighteen years old he and Dromio set out to search for their brothers. Aegeon has been searching, too; unwilling to pass by any city where his son might be, he has come even to Ephesus.

Enter the Duke of Ephesus, with Aegeon the merchant of Syracusa, a Gaoler, and other Attendants.

DUKE   Merchant of Syracusa, plead no more.
It hath in solemn synods been decreed,
Both by the Syracusians and ourselves,
To admit no traffic to our adverse towns:
Nay more — if any born at Ephesus
Be seen at Syracusian marts and fairs;
Again, if any Syracusian born
Come to the bay of Ephesus, he dies,
Unless a thousand marks be levied,
To quit the penalty and to ransom him.
Thy substance, valu'd at the highest rate,
Cannot amount unto a hundred marks.
Therefore by law thou art condemn'd to die.

AEGEON   Yet this my comfort: when your words are done,
My woes end likewise with the evening sun.

DUKE   Well, Syracusian, say in brief the cause

83

Why thou departedst from thy native home,
And for what cause thou cam'st to Ephesus.

AEGEON

A heavier task could not have been impos'd
Than I to speak my griefs unspeakable.
In Syracusa was I born, and wed
Unto a woman, happy but for me.
With her I liv'd in joy, our wealth increas'd
By prosperous voyages I often made
To Epidamnum. There my wife became
A joyful mother of two goodly sons.
That very hour, and in the self-same inn,
A meaner woman was delivered
Of such a burthen male, twins both alike.
Those, for their parents were exceeding poor,

84

I bought, and brought up to attend my sons.
My wife, not meanly proud of two such boys,
Made daily motions for our home return:
Unwilling I agreed. Alas, too soon
We came aboard.
A league from Epidamnum had we sail'd,
Before the always-wind-obeying deep
Gave any tragic instance of our harm:
But longer did we not retain much hope.
The sailors sought for safety by our boat,
And left the ship, then sinking-ripe, to us.
My wife, more careful for the latter-born,
Had fasten'd him unto a small spare mast;
To him one of the other twins was bound,
Whilst I had been like heedful of the other.
The children thus dispos'd, my wife and I
Fasten'd ourselves at either end the mast.
At length the sun, gazing upon the earth,
Dispers'd those vapors that offended us.
The seas wax'd calm, and we discovered
Two ships from far making amain to us:
But ere they came — O let me say no more!

DUKE   Nay, forward, old man — do not break off so,
For we may pity, though not pardon thee.

AEGEON   Ere the ships could meet by twice five leagues,
We were encounter'd by a mighty rock,
Which being violently borne upon,
Our helpful ship was splitted in the midst.
Her part, poor soul, burden'd with lesser weight,
Was carried with more speed before the wind,
And in our sight they three were taken up
By fishermen of Corinth, as we thought.
At length, another ship had seiz'd on us;
And, knowing whom it was their hap to save,
Gave healthful welcome to their shipwreck'd guests,
And would have reft the fishers of their prey,
Had not their bark been very slow of sail;
And therefore homeward did they bend their course.
Thus have you heard me sever'd from my bliss.

DUKE   And, for the sake of them thou sorrowest for,
Do me the favor to dilate at full
What hath befall'n of them and thee till now.

AEGEON   My youngest boy, and yet my eldest care,
At eighteen years became inquisitive
After his brother; and importun'd me

	That his attendant — so his case was like,
	Reft of his brother, but retain'd his name —
	Might bear him company in the quest of him.
	Five summers have I spent in farthest Greece,
	And, coasting homeward, came to Ephesus;
	Hopeless to find, yet loath to leave unsought
	Or that, or any place that harbors men.
	But here must end the story of my life.
DUKE	Hapless Aegeon,
	Though thou art adjudged to the death,
	Yet will I favor thee in what I can;
	I'll limit thee this day to seek thy help.
	Beg thou, or borrow, to make up the sum,
	And live: if no, then thou art doom'd to die.
	Gaoler, take him to thy custody.
GAOLER	I will, my lord.
AEGEON	Hopeless and helpless doth Aegeon wend,
	But to procrastinate his lifeless end. *Exeunt.*

Scene 1

The play itself, which begins now, is quite different from the Prologue with its overtones of tragedy. The play is pure fun, pure farce, with preposterous situations and absurd misunderstandings based on mistaken identities. That is what farce is: a kind of comedy in which improbable circumstances are followed through logically to ridiculous extremes.

By an improbable coincidence two other travelers from Syracuse have arrived in Ephesus — Aegeon's son Antipholus and his servant Dromio. For seven years they have been looking for their brothers. Now they have come to Ephesus. Antipholus sends Dromio on an errand to take some money to their inn for safekeeping. A moment later he is amazed to see Dromio back again, talking nonsense about a wife and a home and dinner, and pretending he knows nothing about the gold.

The audience knows immediately, of course, what the situation is: Antipholus has found the city where his missing twin brother lives. This is not his servant Dromio; this Dromio is the brother's

servant, and he has mistaken Antipholus of Syracuse for his
own master, as Antipholus has mistaken him for his own
Dromio. What a chain of confusions this is going to lead to!

Enter Antipholus of Syracuse and Dromio of Syracuse.

ANTIPHOLUS   Bear this gold to the Centaur, where we host,
OF SYRACUSE   And stay there, Dromio, till I come to thee;
               Within this hour it will be dinnertime;
               Till that, I'll view the manners of the town,
               Peruse the traders, gaze upon the buildings,
               And then return and sleep within mine inn,
               For with long travel I am stiff and weary.
               Get thee away.   *Exit Dromio of Syracuse.*
               I to the world am like a drop of water
               That in the ocean seeks another drop.
               So I, to find a mother and a brother,
               In quest of them, unhappier, lose myself.
               Enter Dromio of Ephesus.
               What now? How chance thou art return'd so soon?

DROMIO OF   Return'd so soon! Rather approach'd too late.
EPHESUS   The capon burns, the pig falls from the spit;
               The clock hath strucken twelve upon the bell;
               My mistress made it one upon my cheek:
               She is so hot, because the meat is cold:
               The meat is cold, because you come not home.

S. ANTIPHOLUS Stop in your wind, sir — tell me this, I pray!
               Where have you left the money that I gave you?

E. DROMO   O — sixpence, that I had o' Wednesday last
               To pay the saddler for my mistress' crupper:
               The saddler had it, sir, I kept it not.

S. ANTIPHOLUS I am not in a sportive humor now.
               Where is the gold I gave in charge to thee?

E. DROMO   To me, sir? Why you gave no gold to me.

S. ANTIPHOLUS Come on, sir knave, have done your foolishness,
               And tell me how thou hast dispos'd thy charge.

E. DROMO   My charge was but to fetch you from the mart
               Home to your house, the Phoenix, sir, to dinner.
               My mistress and her sister stays for you.

S. ANTIPHOLUS Now, as I am a Christian, answer me:
               Where is the thousand marks thou hadst of me?

E. DROMO   I have some marks of yours upon my pate,
               Some of my mistress' marks upon my shoulders,
               But not a thousand marks between you both.

S. ANTIPHOLUS Thy mistress' marks? What mistress, slave, hast thou?

E. DROMO   Your worship's wife, my mistress at the Phoenix;

	She that doth fast till you come home to dinner.	
S. ANTIPHOLUS	What, wilt thou flout me thus unto my face,	
	Being forbid? There, take you that, sir knave. *Strikes him.*	
E. DROMO	What mean you, sir? For God's sake, hold your hands!	
	Nay, an you will not, sir, I'll take my heels.	*Exit.*
S. ANTIPHOLUS	Upon my life, by some device or other,	
	The villain is o'er-raught of all my money.	
	I'll to the Centaur, to go seek this slave.	
	I greatly fear my money is not safe.	*Exit.*

In the scene just ended there was a kind of joking, a kind of playing with words, that is called punning. The word "marks" has several meanings. When Antipholus asked "Where is the thousand marks thou hadst of me?" he used one meaning (a mark is a unit of money), and Dromio in his answer shifted to another meaning (a mark is a visible sign, impression, or trace). There are many puns, and many different kinds of puns, in Shakespeare's plays.

Scene 2

Enter Adriana, wife to Antipholus of Ephesus, with Luciana her sister.

ADRIANA   Neither my husband nor the slave return'd,
That in such haste I sent to seek his master!
Sure, Luciana, it is two o'clock.

LUCIANA   Perhaps some merchant hath invited him,
And from the mart he's somewhere gone to dinner.
Good sister, let us dine, and never fret;
A man is master of his liberty.

ADRIANA   Why should their liberty than ours be more?

LUCIANA   Because their business still lies out o' door.
Here comes your man, now is your husband nigh.
Enter Dromio of Ephesus.

ADRIANA   Say, is your tardy master now at hand?

E. DROMIO   Nay, he's at two hands with me, and that my two ears can witness.

ADRIANA   But say, I prithee, is he coming home?

E. DROMIO   Why, mistress, sure my master is stark mad:
When I desir'd him to come home to dinner,
He ask'd me for a thousand marks in gold:
" 'Tis dinnertime," quoth I; "My gold!" quoth he.
"Your meat doth burn," quoth I; "My gold!" quoth he.
"Will you come home?" quoth I; "My gold!" quoth he,
"Where is the thousand marks I gave thee, villain?"
"The pig," quoth I, "is burn'd"; "My gold!" quoth he.
"My mistress, sir —" quoth I; "Hang up thy mistress!
I know not thy mistress, out on thy mistress!"

LUCIANA   Quoth who?

E. DROMIO   Quoth my master.
"I know," quoth he, "no house, no wife, no mistress."

ADRIANA   Go back again, thou slave, and fetch him home.

E. DROMIO	Go back again, and be new beaten home?
	For God's sake send some other messenger.
ADRIANA	Back, slave, or I will break thy pate across.
E. DROMIO	And he will bless that cross with other beating:
	Between you, I shall have a holy head.
ADRIANA	Hence, prating peasant, fetch thy master home.

Exit Dromio of Ephesus.

LUCIANA	Fie, how impatience loureth in your face!
ADRIANA	His company must do his minions grace,
	Whilst I at home starve for a merry look.
	Hath homely age the alluring beauty took
	From my poor cheek? My decayed fair
	A sunny look of his would soon repair.
	Since that my beauty cannot please his eye,
	I'll weep what's left away and weeping die.
LUCIANA	How many fond fools serve mad jealousy!

Exeunt.

90

Scene 3

Enter Antipholus of Syracuse.

S. ANTIPHOLUS The gold I gave to Dromio is laid up
Safe at the Centaur, and the heedful slave
Is wander'd forth, in care to seek me out.
Enter Dromio of Syracuse.
How now, sir! Is your merry humor alter'd?
As you love strokes, so jest with me again.
You know no Centaur? You receiv'd no gold?
Your mistress sent to have me home to dinner?
My house was at the Phoenix? Wast thou mad,
That thus so madly thou didst answer me?

S. DROMIO What answer, sir? When spake I such a word?

S. ANTIPHOLUS Even now, even here, not half an hour since.

S. DROMIO I did not see you since you sent me hence,
Home to the Centaur, with the gold you gave me.

S. ANTIPHOLUS Villain, thou didst deny the gold's receipt,
And told'st me of a mistress and a dinner —
For which, I hope, thou felt'st I was displeas'd.

S. DROMIO I am glad to see you in this merry vein.
What means this jest? I pray you, master, tell me.

S. ANTIPHOLUS Think'st thou I jest? Hold, take thou that, and that. *Beats him.*

S. DROMIO Hold, sir, for God's sake! Now your jest is earnest.
But, I pray, sir, why am I beaten?

S. ANTIPHOLUS Shall I tell you why?

S. DROMIO Ay, sir, and wherefore; for they say every why hath a wherefore.

S. ANTIPHOLUS Why first, for flouting me; and then wherefore,
For urging it the second time to me.

S. DROMIO Was there ever any man thus beaten out of season,
When in the why and the wherefore is neither rhyme nor reason?
Well, sir, I thank you.

S. ANTIPHOLUS Thank me, sir? For what?

S. DROMIO Marry, sir, for this something that you gave me for nothing.

S. ANTIPHOLUS Well, sir, learn to jest in good time — there's a time for all things. But soft, who wafts us yonder?
Enter Adriana and Luciana.

ADRIANA Ay, ay, Antipholus, look strange, and frown,
Some other mistress hath thy sweet aspects.
The time was once, when thou unurg'd wouldst vow

91

	That never words were music to thine ear,
	That never object pleasing in thine eye,
	That never touch well welcome to thy hand,
	That never meat sweet-savor'd in thy taste,
	Unless I spake, or look'd, or touch'd, or carv'd to thee.
	How comes it now, my husband, O, how comes it,
	That thou art then estranged from thyself?
	Ah, do not tear away thyself from me.
S. ANTIPHOLUS	Plead you to me, fair dame? I know you not:
	In Ephesus I am but two hours old,
	As strange unto your town as to your talk.
LUCIANA	Fie, brother! How the world is chang'd with you.
	When were you wont to use my sister thus?
	She sent for you by Dromio home to dinner.
S. ANTIPHOLUS	By Dromio?
S. DROMIO	By me?
ADRIANA	By thee, and this thou didst return from him —
	That he did buffet thee, and in his blows
	Denied my house for his, me for his wife.
S. ANTIPHOLUS	Did you converse, sir, with this gentlewoman?
	What is the course and drift of your compact?
S. DROMIO	I, sir? I never saw her till this time.
S. ANTIPHOLUS	Villain, thou liest; for even her very words
	Didst thou deliver to me on the mart.
S. DROMIO	I never spake with her in all my life.
S. ANTIPHOLUS	How can she thus then call us by our names?
ADRIANA	How ill agrees it with your gravity
	To counterfeit thus grossly with your slave.
S. ANTIPHOLUS	To me she speaks, she moves me for her theme;
	What, was I married to her in my dream?
	Or sleep I now and think I hear all this?
	What error drives our eyes and ears amiss?
LUCIANA	Dromio, go bid the servants spread for dinner.
S. DROMIO	O, for my beads! I cross me for a sinner.
	This is the fairy land — O spite of spites! —
	We talk with goblins, owls, and sprites;
	If we obey them not, this will ensue:
	They'll suck our breath, or pinch us black and blue.
LUCIANA	Why prat'st thou to thyslf and answer'st not?
ADRIANA	Come, come, no longer will I be a fool,
	To put the finger in the eye and weep,
	Whilst man and master laughs my woes to scorn.
	Come, sir, to dinner. Dromio, keep the gate.
	Sirrah, if any ask you for your master,
	Say he dines forth, and let no creature enter.

	Come, sister; Dromio, play the porter well.	
S. ANTIPHOLUS	Am I in earth, in heaven, or in hell?	
	Sleeping or waking? Mad or well-advis'd?	
	Known unto these, and to myself disguis'd!	
	I'll say as they say, and persever so,	
	And in this mist at all adventures go.	
S. DROMIO	Master, shall I be porter at the gate?	
ADRIANA	Ay, and let none enter, lest I break your pate.	
LUCIANA	Come, come, Antipholus, we dine too late.	*Exeunt.*

Improbable? Of course. The whole play is improbable. It is improbable that Antipholus of Syracuse didn't realize immediately why Adriana thinks he is her husband. It is improbable that twins who have grown up in different cities without knowing each other should talk alike, or happen to dress alike. It is improbable that no one looks for a reasonable explanation for things that make no sense, instead of blaming them on witchcraft. But if everyone behaved rationally, there would be no fun — and no play.

Scene 4

At last the missing husband, Antipholus of Ephesus, arrives home for dinner. He has been out with his friends, but wants his wife to believe he was busy about a chain being made for her. He expects his wife to be a little annoyed by his tardiness, but he certainly does not expect to find himself locked out of his house and disowned by his wife!

Enter Antipholus of Ephesus, his man Dromio of Ephesus, Angelo the goldsmith, and Balthazar a merchant.

E. ANTIPHOLUS	Good Signior Angelo, you must excuse us all —
	My wife is shrewish when I keep not hours;
	Say that I linger'd with you at your shop
	To see the making of her carcanet.
	But here's a villain that would face me down
	He met me on the mart, and that I beat him,
	And charg'd him with a thousand marks in gold,
	And that I did deny my wife and house.
	To Dromio. I think thou art an ass.
E. DROMIO	Marry, so it doth appear
	By the wrongs I suffer, and the blows I bear.
	I should kick, being kick'd, and being at that pass,

	You would keep from my heels, and beware of an ass.
E. ANTIPHOLUS	But soft, my door is lock'd; go bid them let us in.
E. DROMIO	Maud, Bridget, Marian, Cicely, Gillian, Ginn!
S. DROMIO	*Within.* Mome, malt-horse, capon, coxcomb, idiot, patch!
	Either get thee from the door, or sit down at the hatch.
E. ANTIPHOLUS	Who talks within there? Ho, open the door!
S. DROMIO	*Within.* Right, sir; I'll tell you when, an you'll tell me wherefore.
E. ANTIPHOLUS	Wherefore? For my dinner: I have not din'd today.
S. DROMIO	*Within.* Nor today here you must not; come again when you may.
E. ANTIPHOLUS	What art thou that keep'st me out from the house I owe?
S. DROMIO	*Within.* The porter for this time, sir, and my name is Dromio.
E. DROMIO	O villain, thou hast stol'n both mine office and my name!
	The one ne'er got me credit, the other mickle blame.

Antipholus of Ephesus beats upon the door.

E. ANTIPHOLUS	Thou baggage, let me in.
S. DROMIO	*Within.* Can you tell for whose sake?
E. DROMIO	Master, knock the door hard.
S. DROMIO	*Within.* Let him knock till it ache.
ADRIANA	*Within.* Who is that at the door that keeps all this noise?
S. DROMIO	*Within.* By my troth, your town is troubled with unruly boys.
E. ANTIPHOLUS	Are you there, wife? You might have come before.
ADRIANA	*Within.* Your wife, sir knave! Go, get you from the door.
E. ANTIPHOLUS	Go fetch me something — I'll break ope the gate.
S. DROMIO	*Within.* Break any breaking here, and I'll break your knave's pate.
E. ANTIPHOLUS	Go, get thee gone, fetch me an iron crow.
BALTHAZAR	Have patience, sir — O let it not be so!
	Herein you war against your reputation.
	Be rul'd by me, depart in patience,
	And let us to the Porpentine to dinner.
	And, about evening, come yourself alone,
	To know the reason of this strange restraint.
	If by strong hand you offer to break in,
	Now in the stirring passage of the day,
	A vulgar comment will be made of it.
E. ANTIPHOLUS	You have prevail'd. I will depart in quiet,
	And, in despite of mirth, mean to be merry.
	Let us go now to dinner. *To Angelo.* Get you home,
	And fetch the chain — by this, I know, 'tis made —
	Bring it, I pray you, to the Porpentine.
	That chain will I bestow — to spite my wife —
	Upon mine hostess there. Good sir, make haste.
ANGELO	I'll meet you at that place some hour hence.
E. ANTIPHOLUS	Do so. This jest shall cost me some expense. *Exeunt.*

Scene 5

*Another kind of complication develops now. The visiting An-
tipholus from Syracuse, forced to have dinner with Adriana
(who calls herself his wife), finds himself in love with Luciana,
Adriana's sister. Luciana is moved, and puzzled, by his words
of love because they seem to be earnest and honorable, not at*

95

all the words of an unfaithful husband — yet how can they be
otherwise, for he is (she thinks) her sister's husband.

Enter Luciana with Antipholus of Syracuse.

LUCIANA   And may it be that you have quite forgot
A husband's office? Shall, Antipholus,
Even in the spring of love, thy love-springs rot?
Shall love, in building, grow so ruinous?
If you did wed my sister for her wealth,
Then for her wealth's sake use her with more kindness:
Or, if you like elsewhere, do it by stealth,
Muffle your false love with some show of blindness:
Then, gentle brother, get you in again;
Comfort my sister, cheer her, call her wife;
'Tis holy sport to be a little vain,
When the sweet breath of flattery conquers strife.

S. ANTIPHOLUS   Sweet mistress — what your name is else, I know not;
Nor by what wonder you do hit of mine —
Less in your knowledge and your grace you show not
Than our earth's wonder, more than earth divine.
Against my soul's pure truth why labor you
To make it wander in an unknown field?
Are you a god? Would you create me new?
Transform me, then, and to your power I'll yield.
But if that I am I, then well I know
Your weeping sister is no wife of mine,
Nor to her bed no homage do I owe:
Far more, far more, to you do I decline.

LUCIANA   What, are you mad, that you do reason so?

S. ANTIPHOLUS   Not mad, but mated — how, I do not know.

LUCIANA   It is a fault that springeth from your eye.

S. ANTIPHOLUS   For gazing on your beams, fair sun, being by.

LUCIANA   Gaze where you should, and that will clear your sight.

S. ANTIPHOLUS   As good to wink, sweet love, as look on night.

LUCIANA   Why call you me love? Call my sister so.

S. ANTIPHOLUS   Thy sister's sister.

LUCIANA   That's my sister.

S. ANTIPHOLUS   No:
It is thyself, mine own self's better part:
Mine eye's clear eye, my dear heart's dearer heart.
Thee will I love, and with thee lead my life;
Thou hast no husband yet, nor I no wife:
Give me thy hand.

LUCIANA   O, soft, sir, hold you still.
I'll fetch my sister, to get her good will.   *Exit.*

96

Dromio of Syracuse has run into romantic problems too. A great fat kitchen-maid claims him for her own. Therefore, believing that Ephesus is inhabited by witches, Antipholus decides to be gone, and sends Dromio to seek passage for them on the first ship that sails. Before they can get away, however, still one more complication arises. Angelo the goldsmith comes bringing the gold chain, which he insists on giving to Antipholus (of Syracuse).

Enter Dromio of Syracuse, running.

S. ANTIPHOLUS   Why, how now, Dromio! Where run'st thou so fast?

S. DROMIO   Do you know me, sir? Am I Dromio? Am I your man? Am I myself?

S. ANTIPHOLUS   Thou art Dromio, thou art my man, thou art thyself.

S. DROMIO   I am an ass, I am a woman's man, and besides myself.

S. ANTIPHOLUS   What woman's man? And how besides thyself?

S. DROMIO   Marry, sir, besides myself, I am due to a woman; one that claims me, one that haunts me, one that will have me.

S. ANTIPHOLUS   What is she?

S. DROMIO   Marry, sir, she's the kitchen-wench, and all grease — and I know not what use to put her to, but to make a lamp of her, and run from her by her own light.

S. ANTIPHOLUS	What's her name?
S. DROMIO	Nell, sir: but her name and three quarters — that's an ell and three quarters — will not measure her from hip to hip.
S. ANTIPHOLUS	Then she bears some breadth?
S. DROMIO	No longer from head to foot than from hip to hip: she is spherical, like a globe. To conclude, this drudge, or diviner, laid claim to me — called me Dromio, swore I was assur'd to her, told me what privy marks I had about me, as the mark of my shoulder, the mole in my neck, the great wart on my left arm, that I, amaz'd, ran from her as a witch.
S. ANTIPHOLUS	Go, hie thee presently post to the road, And if the wind blow any way from shore, I will not harbor in this town tonight. If any bark put forth, come to the mart, Where I will walk till you return to me. If every one knows us, and we know none, 'Tis time, I think, to trudge, pack, and be gone.
S. DROMIO	As from a bear a man would run for life, So fly I from her that would be my wife. *Exit.*
S. ANTIPHOLUS	There's none but witches do inhabit here, And therefore 'tis high time that I were hence. She that doth call me husband, even my soul Doth for a wife abhor. But her fair sister, Possess'd with such a gentle sovereign grace, Of such enchanting presence and discourse, Hath almost made me traitor to myself: But, lest myself be guilty to self-wrong, I'll stop mine ears against the mermaid's song. *Enter Angelo with the chain.*
ANGELO	Master Antipholus —
S. ANTIPHOLUS	Ay, that's my name.
ANGELO	I know it well, sir. Lo, here is the chain. I thought to have ta'en you at the Porpentine. The chain unfinish'd made me stay thus long.
S. ANTIPHOLUS	What is your will that I shall do with this?
ANGELO	What please yourself, sir: I have made it for you.
S. ANTIPHOLUS	Made it for me, sir! I bespoke it not.
ANGELO	Not once, nor twice, but twenty times you have: Go home with it and please your wife withal, And soon at supper time I'll visit you, And then receive my money for the chain.
S. ANTIPHOLUS	I pray you, sir, receive the money now, For fear you ne'er see chain nor money more.
ANGELO	You are a merry man, sir. Fare you well. *Exit.*
S. ANTIPHOLUS	What I should think of this, I cannot tell:

98

But this I think, there's no man is so vain
That would refuse so fair an offer'd chain.
I see a man here needs not live by shifts,
When in the streets he meets such golden gifts:
I'll to the mart, and there for Dromio stay —
If any ship put out, then straight away.   *Exit.*

*From here on new complications and misunderstandings will
come thick and fast. Always the audience knows more than the
characters know, and it is this knowledge about everything, this
omniscience, that is the source of the humor — because nothing
that happens is funny to the characters involved.*

Scene 6

*Moments after the goldsmith gave the chain to the wrong An-
tipholus he met a merchant to whom he, Angelo, owes money.
The merchant is anxious to leave Ephesus immediately and
wants his money. He threatens to have Angelo arrested unless
he pays what he owes, and Angelo promises to pay as soon as
Antipholus pays him for the chain. At that moment Antipholus
enters — Antipholus of Ephesus, who did* not *receive the chain.*

Enter Angelo with a Merchant and an Officer.

MERCHANT You know since Pentecost the sum is due,
And since I have not much importun'd you,
Nor now I had not, but that I am bound
To Persia, and want guilders for my voyage:
Therefore make present satisfaction,
Or I'll attach you by this officer.

ANGELO Even just the sum that I do owe to you
Is growing to me by Antipholus,
And in the instant that I met with you
He had of me a chain. At five o'clock
I shall receive the money for the same.
Enter Antipholus of Ephesus and Dromio of Ephesus.

E. ANTIPHOLUS While I go to the goldsmith's house, go thou
And buy a rope's end — that will I bestow
Among my wife and her confederates,
For locking me out of my doors by day.
But soft, I see the goldsmith; get thee gone,

99

	Buy thou a rope, and bring it home to me.
	Exit Dromio of Ephesus.
ANGELO	Good Master Antipholus, here is the note
	How much your chain weighs to the utmost carat,
	The fineness of the gold, and chargeful fashion —
	Which doth amount to three odd ducats more
	Than I stand debted to this gentleman.
	I pray you, see him presently discharg'd,
	For he is bound to sea, and stays but for it.
E. ANTIPHOLUS	I am not furnish'd with the present money:
	Besides, I have some business in the town.
	Good signior, take the stranger to my house,
	And with you take the chain, and bid my wife
	Disburse the sum on the receipt thereof.
	Perchance I will be there as soon as you.
ANGELO	Then you will bring the chain to her yourself?
E. ANTIPHOLUS	No, bear it with you, lest I come not time enough.
ANGELO	Well, sir, I will. Have you the chain about you?
E. ANTIPHOLUS	And if I have not, sir, I hope you have:
	Or else you may return without your money.
ANGELO	Come, come, you know I gave it you even now.
E. ANTIPHOLUS	Fie! Now you run this humor out of breath.
	Come, where's the chain? I pray you, let me see it.
MERCHANT	My business cannot brook this dalliance.
	Good sir, say whe'r you'll answer me or no:
	If not, I'll leave him to the officer.
E. ANTIPHOLUS	I answer you! What should I answer you?
ANGELO	The money that you owe me for the chain.
E. ANTIPHOLUS	I owe you none till I receive the chain.
ANGELO	You know I gave it you half an hour since.
E. ANTIPHOLUS	You gave me none, you wrong me much to say so.
ANGELO	You wrong me more, sir, in denying it.
	Consider how it stands upon my credit.
MERCHANT	Well, officer, arrest him at my suit.
OFFICER	I do.
	To Angelo. And charge you in the Duke's name to obey me.
ANGELO	This touches me in reputation.
	Either consent to pay this sum for me,
	Or I attach you by this officer.
E. ANTIPHOLUS	Consent to pay thee that I never had!
	Arrest me, foolish fellow, if thou dar'st.
ANGELO	Here is thy fee, arrest him, officer.
	I would not spare my brother in this case,
	If he should scorn me so apparently.
OFFICER	*To Antipholus.* I do arrest you, sir. You hear the suit.

100

E. ANTIPHOLUS	I do obey thee, till I give thee bail.
	To Angelo. But, sirrah, you shall buy this sport as dear
	As all the metal in your shop will answer.
	Enter Dromio of Syracuse from the Bay.
S. DROMIO	Master, there's a bark of Epidamnum,
	That stays but till her owner comes aboard,
	And then she bears away. Our fraughtage, sir,
	I have convey'd aboard, and I have bought
	The oil, the balsamum, and aqua-vitae.
	The ship is in her trim, the merry wind
	Blows fair from land: they stay for nought at all
	But for their owner, master, and yourself.
E. ANTIPHOLUS	How now! A madman? Why, thou peevish sheep,
	What ship of Epidamnum stays for me?
S. DROMIO	A ship you sent me to, to hire waftage.
E. ANTIPHOLUS	Thou drunken slave, I sent thee for a rope,
	And told thee to what purpose, and what end.
S. DROMIO	You sent me to the Bay, sir, for a bark.
E. ANTIPHOLUS	I will debate this matter at more leisure,
	And teach your ears to list me with more heed.
	To Adriana, villain, hie thee straight:
	Give her this key, and tell her, in the desk
	That's cover'd o'er with Turkish tapestry,
	There is a purse of ducats — let her send it.
	Tell her I am arrested in the street,
	And that shall bail me. Hie thee, slave — be gone.
	On, officer, to prison till it come.
	Exeunt all but Dromio of Syracuse.
S. DROMIO	To Adriana! That is where we din'd,
	Where Dowsabel did claim me for her husband.
	Thither I must, although against my will;
	For servants must their masters' minds fulfill. *Exit.*

Poor Dromio (of Syracuse) is completely bewildered. His troubles began this morning when he was sent on a simple errand by his master: to take some gold to the Centaur. This he did. When he returned, his master was unaccountably angry at him; he accused him of joking about a mistress and a house and dinner, and of denying knowledge of the gold. What's more, two strange women dragged him and his master home with them to dinner. There Dromio found himself in danger of being married to a greasy kitchen-wench. When he and his master escaped from those witches (they must have been witches!) he, Dromio, was sent to arrange passage for them on the first ship leaving this strange land. He found a ship and made the ar-

rangements, just as he was told to do. Now his master seems really to have taken leave of his senses: he shouts that Dromio was sent for a rope, not a ship, and sends him back to that witch-haunted house where they had dinner! Ah, well. A servant must obey his master even when the master makes no sense. And so he goes.

Scene 7

Enter Adriana and Luciana.

ADRIANA	Ah, Luciana, did he tempt thee so?
	Mightst thou perceive a surety in his eye,
	That he did plead in earnest? Yea or no?
	Look'd he or red or pale, or sad or merrily?
LUCIANA	First he denied you had in him no right.
ADRIANA	He meant he did me none: the more my spite.
LUCIANA	Then swore he that he was a stranger here.
ADRIANA	And true he swore, though yet forsworn he were.
LUCIANA	Then pleaded I for you.
ADRIANA	And what said he?
LUCIANA	That love I begg'd for you, he begg'd of me.
ADRIANA	With what persuasion did he tempt thy love?
LUCIANA	With words that in an honest suit might move.
	First, he did praise my beauty, then my speech.
ADRIANA	Didst speak him fair?
LUCIANA	Have patience, I beseech.
ADRIANA	I cannot, nor I will not hold me still.
	My tongue, though not my heart, shall have his will.
	He is deformed, crooked, old, and sere,
	Ill-fac'd, worse bodied, shapeless everywhere.
LUCIANA	Who would be jealous then of such a one?
	No evil lost is wail'd when it is gone.
ADRIANA	Ah, but I think him better than I say;
	And yet would herein others' eyes were worse.
	Far from her nest the lapwing cries away;
	My heart prays for him, though my tongue do curse.
	Enter Dromio of Syracuse.
S. DROMIO	Here, go — the desk, the purse! Sweet now, make haste.
LUCIANA	How hast thou lost thy breath?
S. DROMIO	By running fast.

ADRIANA	Why, man, what is the matter?
S. DROMIO	I do not know the matter, he is 'rested on the case.
ADRIANA	What, is he arrested? Tell me at whose suit.
S. DROMIO	I know not at whose suit he is arrested well;
	But he's in a suit of buff which 'rested him, that can I tell.
	Will you send him, mistress, redemption, the money in the desk?
ADRIANA	Go fetch it, sister. *Exit Luciana.*
	This I wonder at.
	That he, unknown to me, should be in debt.
	Tell me, was he arrested on a band?
S. DROMIO	Not on a band, but on a stronger thing:
	A chain, a chain! Do you not hear it ring?
ADRIANA	What, the chain?
S. DROMIO	No, no, the bell, 'tis time that I were gone!
	It was two ere I left him, and now the clock strikes one.
ADRIANA	The hours come back! That did I never hear.
S. DROMIO	O yes, if any hour meet a sergeant, a turns back for very fear.
ADRIANA	As if Time were in debt! How fondly dost thou reason!
S. DROMIO	Time is a very bankrupt, and owes more than he's worth to season.
	Nay, he's a thief too: have you not heard men say,
	That Time comes stealing on by night and day?
	If Time be in debt and theft, and a sergeant in the way,
	Hath he not reason to turn back an hour in a day?
	Enter Luciana with a purse.
ADRIANA	Go, Dromio. There's the money, bear it straight,
	And bring thy master home immediately. *Exit Dromio.*
	Come, sister. I am press'd down with conceit:
	Conceit, my comfort and my injury. *Exeunt.*

Scene 8

Here is how things stand at the moment for Antipholus of Syracuse: he arrived in Ephesus this morning, a total stranger. Almost from the moment of his arrival odd things have been happening. His servant Dromio has been annoying him with all kinds of practical jokes; for a while he even seemed to be in league with a woman of the city who claimed to be Antipholus's wife and took him home to dinner with her. There Antipholus fell in love with her sister, who would have nothing to do with

him because, she said, he was married to Adriana. Later he was
greeted on the street by a perfect stranger and presented with a
handsome gold chain. Nothing makes any sense. Therefore,
Antipholus is more and more convinced that he has stumbled
into some fairy land. Now, when Dromio appears bringing him
a lot of money and making jokes about Antipholus's being ar-
rested — and even saying that he brought word an hour ago
about the ship! — Antipholus thinks evil spirits have surely taken
possession of Dromio, and resolves that nothing will keep them
in this town overnight.

Enter Antipholus of Syracuse.

S. ANTIPHOLUS   There's not a man I meet but doth salute me
As if I were their well-acquainted friend,
And every one doth call me by my name:
Some tender money to me, some invite me;
Some other give me thanks for kindnesses.
Sure, these are but imaginary wiles,
And Lapland sorcerers inhabit here.
Enter Dromio of Syracuse, running.

S. DROMIO   Master, here's the gold you sent me for. What, where is he that
came behind you, sir?

S. ANTIPHOLUS   What gold is this? Whom dost thou mean?

S. DROMIO   He that came behind you, sir, like an evil angel, and bid you
forsake your liberty.

S. ANTIPHOLUS   I understand thee not.

S. DROMIO   The man, sir, that when gentlemen are tired, 'rests them.

S. ANTIPHOLUS   What, thou mean'st an officer?

S. DROMIO   Ay, sir, one that thinks a man always going to bed, and says,
"God give you good rest!"

S. ANTIPHOLUS   Well, sir, there rest in your foolery. Is there any ship puts forth
tonight? May we be gone?

S. DROMIO   Why, sir, I brought you word an hour since that the bark Expedition put forth tonight, and then were you hinder'd by the
sergeant. Here are the angels that you sent for to deliver you.
He gives Antipholus of Syracuse the money.

S. ANTIPHOLUS   The fellow is distract, and so am I,
And here we wander in illusions:
Some blessed power deliver us from hence!
I will not stay tonight for all the town —
Therefore away, to get our stuff aboard.   *Exeunt.*

Now back to Antipholus who lives here in Ephesus. Everything
has gone wrong for him today. First his wife locked him out
of his house without his dinner. Then Angelo the goldsmith

failed to bring him the chain as he had promised. On top of that, when Angelo finally did appear he pretended he had already given Antipholus the chain, and even had the insolence to have him arrested for refusing to pay for it! A chain he never got!

If only the two Antipholuses, or the two Dromios, could meet each other, everything would straighten itself out — but they just miss. As Antipholus of Syracuse leaves in one direction, Antipholus of Ephesus arrives from another and meets his servant Dromio, his faithful servant, who is bringing the rope he was sent for — and knows nothing about any five hundred ducats Antipholus says he sent him for.

	Enter Antipholus of Ephesus with an Officer.
E. ANTIPHOLUS	Fear me not, man, I will not break away.
	Enter Dromio of Ephesus with a rope's end.
	Here comes my man, I think he brings the money.
	How now, sir! Have you that I sent you for?
E. DROMIO	Here's that, I warrant you, will pay them all.
E. ANTIPHOLUS	But where's the money?
E. DROMIO	Why, sir, I gave the money for the rope.
E. ANTIPHOLUS	Five hundred ducats, villain, for a rope?
	To what end did I bid thee hie thee home?
E. DROMIO	To a rope's end, sir, and to that end am I return'd.
E. ANTIPHOLUS	And to that end, sir, I will welcome you.
	He beats Dromio with the rope.
OFFICER	*To Antipholus.* Good sir, be patient.
E. DROMIO	Nay, 'tis for me to be patient. I am in adversity.
OFFICER	*To Dromio.* Good now, hold thy tongue.
E. DROMIO	Nay, rather persuade him to hold his hands.
E. ANTIPHOLUS	Senseless villain!
E. DROMIO	I would I were senseless, sir, that I might not feel your blows.
E. ANTIPHOLUS	Thou art sensible in nothing but blows, and so is an ass.
E. DROMIO	I am an ass, indeed. I have served him from the hour of my nativity to this instant, and have nothing at his hands for my service but blows. When I am cold, he heats me with beating; when I am warm, he cools me with beating; I am wak'd with it when I sleep, rais'd with it when I sit, driven out of doors with it when I go from home, welcom'd home with it when I return.
	Enter Adriana, Luciana, and a schoolmaster called Pinch.
E. ANTIPHOLUS	*Beating Dromio.* Wilt thou still talk?

Poor Dromio (of Ephesus). And poor Antipholus (of Ephesus). Antipholus's wife Adriana, convinced that he is out of his mind,

105

has found a schoolmaster-conjurer to drive out the evil spirits that possess him. A schoolmaster would, of course, know Latin and therefore be able to communicate with the spirits, who were supposed to speak only Latin. When Pinch tries to take him in hand, Antipholus becomes violent. He has had about all that he can stand today — from his servant, from the goldsmith, from the sergeant — and above all from his wife!

ADRIANA	How say you now? Is not my husband mad?
	Good Doctor Pinch, you are a conjurer —
	Establish him in his true sense again,
	And I will please you what you will demand.
LUCIANA	Alas, how fiery and how sharp he looks!
PINCH	*To Antipholus.* Give me your hand, and let me feel your pulse.
E. ANTIPHOLUS	There is my hand, and let it feel your ear. *Strikes Pinch.*

106

PINCH	I charge thee, Satan, hous'd within this man,
	To yield possession to my holy prayers,
	And to thy state of darkness hie thee straight.
	I conjure thee by all the saints in heaven.
E. ANTIPHOLUS	Peace, doting wizard, peace; I am not mad.
ADRIANA	O that thou wert not, poor distressed soul!
E. ANTIPHOLUS	Did this companion with the saffron face
	Revel and feast it at my house today,
	Whilst upon me the guilty doors were shut,
	And I denied to enter in my house?
ADRIANA	O husband, God doth know you din'd at home.
E. ANTIPHOLUS	Din'd at home! *To Dromio.* Thou villain, what say'st thou?
E. DROMIO	Sir, sooth to say, you did not dine at home.
E. ANTIPHOLUS	Were not my doors lock'd up, and I shut out?
E. DROMIO	Perdie, your doors were lock'd, and you shut out.
E. ANTIPHOLUS	And did not she herself revile me there?
E. DROMIO	Sans fable, she herself revil'd you there.
E. ANTIPHOLUS	And did not I in rage depart from thence?
E. DROMIO	In verity, you did depart from thence.
E. ANTIPHOLUS	*To Adriana.* Thou hast suborn'd the goldsmith to arrest me.
ADRIANA	Alas, I sent you money to redeem you,
	By Dromio here, who came in haste for it.
E. DROMIO	Money by me! Heart and good will you might,
	But surely, master, not a rag of money.
E. ANTIPHOLUS	Went'st not thou to her for a purse of ducats?
ADRIANA	He came to me, and I deliver'd it.
LUCIANA	And I am witness with her that she did.
E. DROMIO	God and the ropemaker bear me witness
	That I was sent for nothing but a rope.
PINCH	Mistress, both man and master is possess'd —
	I know it by their pale and deadly looks.
	They must be bound, and laid in some dark room.
E. ANTIPHOLUS	*To Adriana.* Say, wherefore didst thou lock me forth today?
	To Dromio. And why dost thou deny the bag of gold?
ADRIANA	I did not, gentle husband, lock thee forth.
E. DROMIO	And, gentle master, I receiv'd no gold:
	But I confess, sir, that we were lock'd out.
ADRIANA	Dissembling villain, thou speak'st false in both.
E. ANTIPHOLUS	Dissembling harlot, thou art false in all,
	And art confederate with a damned pack,
	To make a loathsome abject scorn of me;
	But with these nails I'll pluck out these false eyes
	That would behold in me this shameful sport.
	Enter three or four, and offer to bind him. He strives.
ADRIANA	O, bind him, bind him, let him not come near me.

PINCH	More company! The fiend is strong within him.
LUCIANA	Ay me! Poor man, how pale and wan he looks.
E. ANTIPHOLUS	What, will you murther me? Thou gaoler, thou,
	I am thy prisoner; wilt thou suffer them
	To make a rescue?
OFFICER	Masters, let him go:
	He is my prisoner, and you shall not have him.
PINCH	Go, bind this man, for he is frantic too.
	They bind Dromio of Ephesus.
ADRIANA	What wilt thou do, thou peevish officer?
	Hast thou delight to see a wretched man
	Do outrage and displeasure to himself?
OFFICER	He is my prisoner — if I let him go,
	The debt he owes will be requir'd of me.
ADRIANA	I will discharge thee ere I go from thee.
	To Pinch. Good Master Doctor, see him safe convey'd
	Home to my house. O most unhappy day!

E. ANTIPHOLUS	Out on thee, villain! Wherefore dost thou mad me?
E. DROMIO	Will you be bound for nothing? Be mad, good master — Cry, "The devil!"
LUCIANA	God help, poor souls, how idly do they talk.
ADRIANA	Go bear him hence. Sister, go you with me.
	Pinch and his assistants exeunt with Antipholus of Ephesus and Dromio of Ephesus.
ADRIANA	Say now, whose suit is he arrested at?
OFFICER	One Angelo a goldsmith, do you know him?
ADRIANA	I know the man. What is the sum he owes?
OFFICER	Two hundred ducats.
ADRIANA	Say, how grows it due?
OFFICER	Due for a chain your husband had of him.
ADRIANA	He did bespeak a chain for me, but had it not. Bear me forthwith unto his creditor, And, knowing how the debt grows, I will pay it. *Exeunt.*

Finale

By now the day has passed and it is almost sundown, almost time for poor old Aegeon, the father of the two Antipholuses, to die, unless someone comes to his aid. He has two sons here in Ephesus, but he cannot look to them for help because they do not know of his danger and there is little chance of their learning of it. One of them is not even aware of Aegeon's existence and the other will soon be gone.

Antipholus and Dromio of Syracuse are on the point of leaving without having discovered that the brothers they seek are actually here in Ephesus. All day they have been on the verge of meeting them and always they have missed. Now that their brothers have been locked up as madmen any chance of meeting is apparently gone, and with it any chance of clearing up the misunderstandings that have developed today. But, at least, the confusion can become no worse. Or can it?

Enter Angelo and the Merchant.

ANGELO	I am sorry, sir, that I have hinder'd you, But I protest he had the chain of me, Though most dishonestly he doth deny it.

MERCHANT	How is the man esteem'd here in the city?
ANGELO	Of very reverent reputation, sir,
	Of credit infinite, highly belov'd,
	Second to none that lives here in the city:
	His word might bear my wealth at any time.
MERCHANT	Speak softly — yonder, as I think, he walks.

Enter Antipholus of Syracuse and Dromio of Syracuse.

ANGELO	'Tis so; and that self chain about his neck,
	Which he forswore most monstrously to have.
	Signior Antipholus, I wonder much
	That you would put me to this shame and trouble,
	And not without some scandal to yourself.
	This chain you had of me, can you deny it?
S. ANTIPHOLUS	I think I had. I never did deny it.
MERCHANT	Yes, that you did, sir, and forswore it too.
S. ANTIPHOLUS	Who heard me to deny it or forswear it?
MERCHANT	These ears of mine, thou knowest, did hear thee.
S. ANTIPHOLUS	Thou art a villain to impeach me thus.
	I'll prove mine honor and mine honesty
	Against thee presently, if thou dar'st stand.
MERCHANT	I dare, and do defy thee for a villain.

They draw. Enter Adriana, Luciana, and others.

LUCIANA	God, for thy mercy! They are loose again.
ADRIANA	Hold, hurt him not for God's sake! He is mad.
	Some get within him, take his sword away.
	Bind Dromio too, and bear them to my house.
S. DROMIO	Run, master, run — for God's sake take a house —
	This is some priory — in — or we are spoil'd.

Exeunt Antipholus and Dromio to the Priory.

Enter the Lady Abbess.

ABBESS	Be quiet, people. Wherefore throng you hither?
ADRIANA	To fetch my poor distracted husband hence.
	Let us come in, that we may bind him fast,
	And bear him home for his recovery.
ANGELO	I knew he was not in his perfect wits.
MERCHANT	I am sorry now that I did draw on him.
ADRIANA	Good people, enter and lay hold on him.
ABBESS	No, not a creature enters in my house.
ADRIANA	Then, let your servants bring my husband forth.
ABBESS	Neither. He took this place for sanctuary,
	And it shall privilege him from your hands
	Till I have brought him to his wits again,
	Or lose my labor in assaying it.
ADRIANA	I will attend my husband, be his nurse,
	Diet his sickness, for it is my office,

	And therefore let me have him home with me.
ABBESS	Be patient, for I will not let him stir
	Till I have used the approved means I have,
	With wholesome syrups, drugs, and holy prayers,
	To make of him a formal man again:
	It is a branch and parcel of mine oath,
	A charitable duty of my order;
	Therefore depart, and leave him here with me.
ADRIANA	I will not hence, and leave my husband here:
	And ill it doth beseem your holiness
	To separate the husband and the wife.

ABBESS   Be quiet and depart, thou shalt not have him.   *Exit.*

LUCIANA   Complain unto the Duke of this indignity.

ADRIANA   Come, go, I will fall prostrate at his feet,
           And never rise, until my tears and prayers
           Have won his Grace to come in person hither,
           And take perforce my husband from the abbess.

MERCHANT   By this, I think, the dial points at five:
           Anon, I'm sure, the Duke himself in person
           Comes this way to the melancholy vale,
           The place of death and sorry execution,
           Behind the ditches of the abbey here.

ANGELO   Upon what cause?

MERCHANT   To see a reverend Syracusian merchant,
           Who put unluckily into this Bay
           Against the laws and statutes of this town,
           Beheaded publicly for his offense.

ANGELO   See where they come. We will behold his death.

LUCIANA   Kneel to the Duke before he pass the abbey.

           *Enter the Duke of Ephesus and Aegeon the merchant of Syra-
           cuse, with the Headsman and other Officers.*

DUKE   Yet once again proclaim it publicly,
           If any friend will pay the sum for him,
           He shall not die — so much we tender him.

ADRIANA   Justice, most sacred Duke, against the abbess!

DUKE   She is a virtuous and a reverend lady.
           It cannot be that she hath done thee wrong.

ADRIANA   May it please your Grace, Antipholus, my husband —
           Whom I made lord of me and all I had
           At your important letters — this ill day
           A most outrageous fit of madness took him:
           That desp'rately he hurried through the street —
           With him his bondman all as mad as he —
           Doing displeasure to the citizens.
           Once did I get him bound, and sent him home.

Anon, I wot not by what strong escape,
He broke from those that had the guard of him,
And with his mad attendant then he fled
Into this abbey, whither we pursu'd them;
And here the abbess shuts the gates on us,
And will not suffer us to fetch him out,
Nor send him forth that we may bear him hence.
Therefore, most gracious Duke, with thy command,
Let him be brought forth and borne hence for help.

DUKE Go, some of you, knock at the abbey gate,
And bid the lady abbess come to me.
I will determine this before I stir.
Enter a Messenger.

MESSENGER O mistress, mistress! Shift and save yourself.
My master and his man are both broke loose,
Beaten the maids a-row, and bound the doctor,

112

	Whose beard they have sing'd off with brands of fire.
	And, sure, unless you send some present help,
	Between them they will kill the conjurer.
ADRIANA	Peace, fool, thy master and his man are here,
	And that is false thou dost report to us.
MESSENGER	Mistress, upon my life, I tell you true,
	I have not breath'd almost since I did see it.
	He cries for you and vows, if he can take you,
	To scorch your face, and to disfigure you.
	Cries are heard from within.
	Hark, hark, I hear him, mistress! Fly, be gone.
DUKE	Come, stand by me, fear nothing. Guard with halberds!
ADRIANA	Ay me, it is my husband! Witness you,
	That he is borne about invisible!
	Even now we hous'd him in the abbey here;
	And now he's there, past thought of human reason.
	Enter Antipholus of Ephesus and Dromio of Ephesus.
E. ANTIPHOLUS	Justice, most gracious Duke! O grant me justice.
AEGEON	Unless the fear of death doth make me dote,
	I see my son Antipholus, and Dromio.
E. ANTIPHOLUS	Justice, sweet prince, against that woman there!
	She whom thou gav'st to me to be my wife.
	Beyond imagination is the wrong
	That she this day hath shameless thrown on me.
DUKE	Discover how, and thou shalt find me just.
E. ANTIPHOLUS	This day, great Duke, she shut the doors upon me,
	While she with harlots feasted in my house.
DUKE	A grievous fault. Say, woman, didst thou so?
ADRIANA	No, my good lord. Myself, he, and my sister
	Today did dine together. So befall my soul
	As this is false he burthens me withal!
LUCIANA	Ne'er may I look on day, nor sleep on night,
	But she tells to your highness simple truth.
ANGELO	O perjur'd woman! They are both forsworn.
	In this the madman justly chargeth them.
E. ANTIPHOLUS	My liege, I am advised what I say.
	This woman lock'd me out this day from dinner;
	That goldsmith there, were he not pack'd with her,
	Could witness it — for he was with me then,
	Who parted with me to go fetch a chain,
	Promising to bring it to the Porpentine,
	Where Balthazar and I did dine together.
	Our dinner done, and he not coming thither,
	I went to seek him. In the street I met him,
	And in his company that gentleman.

There did this perjur'd goldsmith swear me down
That I this day of him receiv'd the chain,
Which, God he knows, I saw not; for the which,
He did arrest me with an officer.
I did obey, and sent my peasant home
For certain ducats: he with none return'd.
Then fairly I bespoke the officer
To go in person with me to my house.
By th' way we met my wife, her sister,
And with them one Pinch, a lean-fac'd villain,
A mere anatomy, a mountebank,
A living dead man. This pernicious slave,
Forsooth, took on him as a conjurer;
And, gazing in mine eyes, feeling my pulse,
Cries out, I was possess'd. Then all together
They fell upon me, bound me, bore me thence,
And in a dark and dankish vault at home
There left me and my man, both bound together —
Till gnawing with my teeth my bonds in sunder,
I gain'd my freedom, and immediately
Ran hither to your Grace, whom I beseech
To give me ample satisfaction
For these deep shames and great indignities.

ANGELO   My lord, in truth, thus far I witness with him:
              That he din'd not at home, but was lock'd out.

DUKE   But had he such a chain of thee or no?

ANGELO   He had, my lord, and when he ran in here,
              These people saw the chain about his neck.

MERCHANT   Besides, I will be sworn these ears of mine
              Heard you confess you had the chain of him,
              After you first forswore it on the mart,
              And, thereupon, I drew my sword on you;
              And then you fled into this abbey here,
              From whence, I think, you are come by miracle.

E. ANTIPHOLUS I never came within these abbey walls,
              Nor ever didst thou draw thy sword on me;
              I never saw the chain, so help me Heaven!
              And this is false you burthen me withal.

DUKE   Why, what an intricate impeach is this!
              If here you hous'd him, here he would have been;
              If he were mad, he would not plead so coldly.
              You say he din'd at home, the goldsmith here
              Denies that saying. Call the abbess hither.
              I think you are all mated, or stark mad.

                                    Exit one to call the Abbess.

114

AEGEON	Most mighty Duke, vouchsafe me speak a word:
	Haply I see a friend will save my life.
DUKE	Speak freely, Syracusian, what thou wilt.
AEGEON	Is not your name, sir, call'd Antipholus?
	And is not that your bondman Dromio?
E. DROMIO	Within this hour I was his bondman, sir,
	But he, I thank him, gnaw'd in two my cords.
	Now am I Dromio, and his man, unbound.
AEGEON	I am sure you both of you remember me.
E. DROMIO	Ourselves we do remember, sir, by you:
	For lately we were bound, as you are now.
	You are not Pinch's patient, are you, sir?
AEGEON	Why look you strange on me? You know me well.
E. ANTIPHOLUS	I never saw you in my life till now.
AEGEON	O, grief hath chang'd me since you saw me last:
	But tell me yet, dost thou not know my voice?
E. ANTIPHOLUS	Neither.
AEGEON	Dromio, nor thou?
E. DROMIO	No, trust me, sir, nor I.
AEGEON	Not know my voice! — O, I cannot err —
	Tell me thou art my son Antipholus.
E. ANTIPHOLUS	I never saw my father in my life.
AEGEON	But seven years since, in Syracusa, boy,
	Thou know'st we parted.
E. ANTIPHOLUS	The Duke can witness with me:
	I ne'er saw Syracusa in my life.

And now the Abbess re-enters — with another Antipholus and Dromio. At long last all the confusions and misunderstandings are cleared up. Twin finds his missing twin, twice over. Aegeon is reunited with his wife. And all ends happily, as a comedy should.

Enter the Abbess, with Antipholus of Syracuse and Dromio of Syracuse. All gather to see them.

ABBESS	Most mighty Duke, behold a man much wrong'd.
ADRIANA	I see two husbands, or mine eyes deceive me.
DUKE	One of these men is Genius to the other:
	And so of these. Which is the natural man,
	And which the spirit? Who deciphers them?
S. DROMIO	I, sir, am Dromio — command him away.
E. DROMIO	I, sir, am Dromio — pray let me stay.
S. ANTIPHOLUS	Aegeon art thou not? Or else his ghost?
S. DROMIO	O, my old master! Who hath bound him here?
ABBESS	Whoever bound him, I will loose his bonds,

	And gain a husband by his liberty.
	Speak, old Aegeon, if thou be'st the man
	That hadst a wife once call'd Aemilia.
AEGEON	If I dream not, thou art Aemilia.
	If thou art she, tell me where is that son
	That floated with thee on the fatal raft?
ABBESS	By men of Epidamnum, he and I
	And the twin Dromio, all were taken up;
	But by and by rude fishermen of Corinth
	By force took Dromio and my son from them.
	What then became of them, I cannot tell.
DUKE	Why, here begins his morning story right:
	These two Antipholuses, these two so like,
	And these two Dromios, one in semblance —
	Besides her urging of her wreck at sea —
	These are the parents to these children,
	Which accidentally are met together.
	Antipholus, thou cam'st from Corinth first.
S. ANTIPHOLUS	No, sir not I. I came from Syracuse.
DUKE	Stay, stand apart — I know not which is which.
E. ANTIPHOLUS	I came from Corinth, my most gracious lord.
E. DROMIO	And I with him.
E. ANTIPHOLUS	Brought to this town by your renowned uncle.
ADRIANA	Which of you two did dine with me today?
S. ANTIPHOLUS	I, gentle mistress.
ADRIANA	And are not you my husband?
E. ANTIPHOLUS	No, I say nay to that.
S. ANTIPHOLUS	And so do I, yet did she call me so;
	And this fair gentlewoman, her sister here,
	Did call me brother. *To Luciana.* What I told you then,
	I hope I shall have leisure to make good,
	If this be not a dream I see and hear.
ANGELO	That is the chain, sir, which you had of me.
S. ANTIPHOLUS	I think it be, sir, I deny it not.
E. ANTIPHOLUS	And you, sir, for this chain arrested me.
ANGELO	I think I did, sir, I deny it not.
ADRIANA	I sent you money, sir, to be your bail,
	By Dromio — but I think he brought it not.
E. DROMIO	No, none by me.
S. ANTIPHOLUS	This purse of ducats I receiv'd from you,
	And Dromio my man did bring them me.
	I see we still did meet each other's man,
	And I was ta'en for him, and he for me;
	And thereupon these errors are arose.

116

E. ANTIPHOLUS	These ducats pawn I for my father here.
DUKE	It shall not need, thy father hath his life.
AEMILIA	Renowned Duke, vouchsafe to take the pains
	To go with us into the abbey here,
	And hear at large discoursed all our fortunes.
	The Duke, my husband, and my children both,
	And you the calendars of their nativity,
	And all that are assembled in this place,
	Go to a gossips' feast, and joy with me
	After so long grief such festivity!
DUKE	With all my heart I'll gossip at this feast.

Exeunt all but the four brothers.

S. DROMIO	Master, shall I fetch your stuff from shipboard?
E. ANTIPHOLUS	Dromio, what stuff of mine hast thou embark'd?
S. DROMIO	Your goods that lay at host, sir, in the Centaur.
S. ANTIPHOLUS	He speaks to me. I am your master, Dromio.
	Come, go with us, we'll look to that anon.
	Embrace thy brother there, rejoice with him.

Exeunt the two Antipholuses.

E. DROMIO	Methinks you are my glass, and not my brother:
	I see by you I am a sweet-fac'd youth.

	Will you walk in to see their gossiping?
s. DROMIO	Not I, sir, you are my elder.
e. DROMIO	That's a question — how shall we try it?
s. DROMIO	We'll draw cuts for the senior — till then lead thou first.
e. DROMIO	Nay, then, thus. *They join hands.*

We came into the world like brother and brother;
And now let's go hand in hand, not one before another.

Exeunt.

4

The Tragedy of Macbeth

The Seen and the Unseen

4

In Shakespeare's day the beliefs men held were a strange combination of ancient mixed with modern, of pagan mixed with Christian. Sorcerers held the power of life or death over others; the devil entered into dead men's bodies and walked abroad; witches were transported through the air, invisible, while their bodies lay senseless in a trance; and every strange happening was an omen of the future. All this was widely believed in the very age when new discoveries in science and geography, new ideas in politics and philosophy, were beginning to move civilization out of that long, stagnant phase we call the Middle Ages.

The pagan gods of Britain — gods of the sun and the moon, of earth and water — were far older than Christianity, and they would not die easily. Christianity had been brought to Britain by missionaries more than a thousand years before Shakespeare was born. For long years, turning into centuries, they and others after them labored to convert the people of Britain to the new religion. Finally, in the year 1030, King Canute had to forbid people "to worship the heathen gods, or sun or moon, fire or flood, wells or stones or trees of any kind, or to love witchcraft, or to practice anything in the way of sacrifice or soothsaying or such delusions." But people are not always able to believe just what their rulers think is best for them.

By the sixteenth century Christianity had been the official religion of England for hundreds of years. Yet under the thin crust of Christian dogma there still seethed and bubbled a mass of superstitious beliefs in sorceries, fairies, spirits, ghosts, demons, devils, and witches.

To the people of Shakespeare's time this unseen world of spirits seemed as real as the visible world around them. What matter that no one had ever seen ghosts or goblins or fairies? They thought they had. When there were unseasonable floods, cold weather in summer, or warm weather in winter, people believed it was because fairies were angry. They believed that sudden violent storms on land or sea were raised by spirits. If a person became strangely confused or bewildered, he thought he was possessed by evil spirits. If wasting illness or dire misfortune visited him, he was sure he had been bewitched — and many a poor old woman was drowned or burned or hanged as a witch on just such flimsy evidence.

It was not only the ignorant country folk, however, who believed in interaction between the seen and the unseen worlds. Most educated men of the sixteenth century accepted a pseudoscientific conception of the universe which itself supported belief in supernatural causes.

Today few children get far beyond the first grade without knowing, first, that the earth is one of nine planets spinning around the sun; second, that the sun is just one of billions of stars in a huge cluster of stars called a galaxy; and third, that there are untold numbers of galaxies in the universe. But almost four hundred years ago, when Shakespeare was writing plays for the theaters of London, few people even dreamed of such a universe. In 1543 Copernicus had first suggested that the sun, not the earth, was the center of the universe, but no one paid much attention. If they noticed at all, they argued against such a ridiculous notion. They kept right on believing, as men had believed for thousands of years, that the earth was the center. Obviously!

Ever since Aristotle, about two thousand years before Shakespeare's time, men

THE UNIVERSE

According to Ptolemy, c. 150 A.D.
Based on theories of Aristotle, c. 350 B.C.

had thought of the universe as a series of concentric spheres, one inside the other, much like one of those wooden eggs that so delight a small child: when he takes the egg apart, he finds a smaller egg inside; inside that is another, still smaller; and so on, down to the tiny chick in the center. According to these theories, the earth was at the very center of the universe (like the chick in the egg) with the sun, the moon, and the stars revolving around it. Men believed that the earth was surrounded by eight spheres, one outside the other. Closest to the earth was the Moon's sphere; outside the Moon's sphere were the spheres of Mercury, Venus, the Sun (midway between the earth and the stars), then Mars, Jupiter, Saturn, and the fixed stars, in that order. The whole structure was enclosed in an outer sphere, called in Latin the *primum mobile* (meaning "first mover"), which made a complete rotation from west to east every twenty-four hours. That motion set all the other spheres rotating, in the opposite direction; hence the name. As the celestial spheres rotated, they rubbed against each other, producing beautiful musical tones called the Music of the Spheres. Outside and above the outer rim of the Universe was the Empyrean Heaven, the abode of God.

Men believed, further, that the same kind of order they saw in the heavens was reflected in the rank-ordering of all things in nature. At the top of the hierarchy was God; at the bottom were inanimate objects, such as stones. In between, all other created beings were ranked in this order: angels, men, animals, and plants.

To complete their misconception of the universe, men believed that just as the heavenly spheres have degree from highest to lowest, and all created beings have degree from highest to lowest, so too do men have degree from highest to lowest: first and highest, of course, was the King. After the King came gentlemen, then citizens, artisans, and, last of all, laborers and slaves. Everyone believed that men were born to these various degrees, and it was against nature for a man to try to move from one class to another.

Their universe was neat and tidy, with a place for everything. So long as everything stayed in its place, all was well. For along with the belief that everything had its proper place, there went a belief in interaction between the heavens, the earth, and society. Man's fate was determined by the stars, yet, at the same time, what a man did could influence the heavens. If a man did anything not proper to his degree — anything unnatural — all nature was thrown out of joint. If a servant raised his hand against his master, or a subject plotted the overthrow of his king, then comets would whiz through the sky, owls would hoot at midday, ghosts would shriek, winds blow, and the earth quake.

Those were some of the beliefs most men held when Shakespeare wrote *Macbeth*, a play in which the natural and the supernatural were woven together to produce a design as black as night and as red as blood, full of witchcraft and foul murder.

The Tragedy of Macbeth

4

The Characters:

DUNCAN, King of Scotland
MALCOLM ⎫
DONALBAIN ⎬ his sons
MACBETH ⎫
BANQUO ⎬ generals of the King's army
MACDUFF ⎫
LENNOX ⎪
ROSS ⎪
MENTETH ⎬ noblemen of Scotland
ANGUS ⎪
CATHNESS ⎭
FLEANCE, son to Banquo
SIWARD, Earl of Northumberland, general of the English forces
YOUNG SIWARD, his son
SEYTON, an officer attending on Macbeth
A DOCTOR
A CAPTAIN
A PORTER
TWO MURTHERERS
LADY MACBETH
GENTLEWOMAN ATTENDING ON LADY MACBETH
THREE WITCHES
LORDS, GENTLEMEN, SOLDIERS, ATTENDANTS, APPARITIONS

The Scene: Scotland and England

"After Malcolme, succeeded Duncane the sonne of his daughter Beatrice: for Malcolme had two daughters, the one, which was this Beatrice, being given in marriage unto one Abbanath Crinen thane of the Iles and west part of Scotland, bare of that marriage the foresaid Duncane; the other called Doada, was married unto Sinel the thane of Glamis, by whom she had issue one Makbeth a valiant gentleman, and one that if he had not been somewhat cruel of nature, might have been thought most worthy the government of a realme."

So write Holinshed in his Chronicles of England, Scotland, and Ireland, *which Shakespeare undoubtedly read. Shakespeare chose as the hero of one of his greatest tragedies the second of those two cousins, Duncan and Macbeth.*

The Malcolm mentioned above, King Malcolm II, had been successful in uniting under his rule almost all of Scotland except some western portions. When Malcolm died in 1034 his grandson Duncan succeeded to the throne; Duncan inherited also (from his father) the title to those independent western lands. Thereby Scotland became for the first time a single united kingdom, and Duncan was its first king. He reigned for only six years, years of almost constant war against invading Norsemen and rebellious lords (thanes). One of Duncan's bravest generals in these wars was his cousin Macbeth.

Shakespeare begins his play toward the end of those wars. His Macbeth is a valiant soldier; he is also an ambitious man and a superstitious one, easily influenced by the powers of darkness. On a barren heath Macbeth has a fateful meeting. Holinshed (whose Chronicles *were sometimes more legend than history) records that meeting and adds: "opinion was these women were the weird sisters, that is (as ye would say) the goddesses of destiny," or (as we would say) the three Fates.*

ACT I

Scene 1

Thunder and lightning. Enter three Witches.

FIRST WITCH	When shall we three meet again?
	In thunder, lightning, or in rain?
SECOND WITCH	When the hurlyburly's done,
	When the battle's lost and won.
THIRD WITCH	That will be ere the set of sun.
FIRST WITCH	Where the place?
SECOND WITCH	Upon the heath.
THIRD WITCH	There to meet with Macbeth.
ALL THREE	Fair is foul, and foul is fair:
	Hover through the fog and filthy air. *Exeunt.*

Alarum within. Enter King Duncan, Malcolm, Donalbain,

Lennox, with Attendants, meeting a bleeding Captain.

DUNCAN What bloody man is that? He can report,
As seemeth by his plight, of the revolt
The newest state.

MALCOLM   This is the sergeant
Who like a good and hardy soldier fought
'Gainst my captivity. Hail, brave friend!
Say to the King the knowledge of the broil
As thou didst leave it.

CAPTAIN   Doubtful it stood,
As two spent swimmers, that do cling together
And choke their art.
Norway himself, with terrible numbers,
Assisted by that most disloyal traitor
The Thane of Cawdor, began a dismal conflict.
No sooner Justice had, with valor arm'd,
Compell'd these skipping kerns to trust their heels,
But the Norwayan lord, surveying vantage,
With furbish'd arms and new supplies of men
Began a fresh assault.

DUNCAN Dismay'd not this our captains, Macbeth and Banquo?

CAPTAIN Yes, as sparrows eagles,
Or the hare the lion.
For brave Macbeth — well he deserves that name —
Disdaining Fortune, with his brandish'd steel,
Which smok'd with bloody execution,
Like Valor's minion carv'd out his passage,
Till he fac'd the slave; and to conclude,
The victory fell on us.

DUNCAN   Great happiness!
No more that Thane of Cawdor shall deceive
Our bosom interest. Go pronounce his present death,
And with his former title greet Macbeth.

ROSS I'll see it done.

DUNCAN What he hath lost noble Macbeth hath won.   *Exeunt.*
Drum within. Enter the three Witches.

THIRD WITCH A drum! A drum!
Macbeth doth come.

ALL THREE The weird sisters, hand in hand,
Posters of the sea and land,
Thus do go about, about,
Thrice to thine, and thrice to mine,
And thrice again, to make up nine.
Peace! The charm's wound up.
Enter Macbeth and Banquo.

124

MACBETH	So foul and fair a day I have not seen.
BANQUO	What are these, so wither'd and so wild
	In their attire?
MACBETH	Speak, if you can: what are you?
FIRST WITCH	All hail, Macbeth, hail to thee, Thane of Glamis!
SECOND WITCH	All hail, Macbeth, hail to thee, Thane of Cawdor!
THIRD WITCH	All hail, Macbeth, that shalt be King hereafter.
BANQUO	Good sir, why do you start, and seem to fear
	Things that do sound so fair? I' th' name of truth,
	Are ye fantastical, or that indeed
	Which outwardly ye show? My noble partner
	You greet with present grace and great prediction
	Of noble having and of royal hope.
	Speak then to me, who neither beg nor fear
	Your favors nor your hate.
FIRST WITCH	Hail!
SECOND WITCH	Hail!
THIRD WITCH	Hail!
FIRST WITCH	Lesser than Macbeth, and greater.
SECOND WITCH	Not so happy, yet much happier.
THIRD WITCH	Thou shalt get Kings, though thou be none.
	So, all hail, Macbeth and Banquo!
FIRST WITCH	Banquo and Macbeth, all hail!
MACBETH	Stay, you imperfect speakers, tell me more.
	By Sinel's death I know I am Thane of Glamis;
	But how of Cawdor? The Thane of Cawdor lives,
	A prosperous gentleman; and to be King
	Stands not within the prospect of belief
	No more than to be Cawdor. Say from whence
	You owe this strange intelligence. Speak, I charge you.
	The Witches vanish.
BANQUO	The earth hath bubbles, as the water has,
	And these are of them. Whither are they vanish'd?
MACBETH	Into the air, and what seem'd corporal
	Melted, as breath into the wind.
	Would they had stay'd.
BANQUO	Were such things here as we do speak about?
	Or have we eaten on the insane root
	That takes the reason prisoner?
MACBETH	Your children shall be Kings.
BANQUO	You shall be King.
MACBETH	And Thane of Cawdor too; went it not so?
BANQUO	To th' selfsame tune and words. Who's here?
	Enter Ross and Angus.
ROSS	The King hath happily receiv'd, Macbeth,

126

	The news of thy success.
ANGUS	And we are sent
	To give thee from our royal master thanks.
ROSS	And, for an earnest of a greater honor,
	He bade me, from him, call thee Thane of Cawdor;
	In which addition, hail, most worthy thane!
	For it is thine.
BANQUO	What, can the devil speak true?
MACBETH	The Thane of Cawdor lives;
	Why do you dress me in borrow'd robes?
ANGUS	Who was the thane lives yet;
	But under heavy judgment bears that life
	He deserves to lose.
MACBETH	*Aside.* Glamis, and Thane of Cawdor.
BANQUO	Cousins, a word, I pray you.
MACBETH	*Aside.* Two truths are told,
	As happy prologues to the swelling act
	Of the imperial theme.
	To Ross and Angus. I thank you, gentlemen.
	Aside. This supernatural soliciting
	Cannot be ill, cannot be good; if ill,
	Why hath it given me earnest of success,
	Commencing in a truth? I am Thane of Cawdor.
	If good, why do I yield to that suggestion
	Whose horrid image doth unfix my hair
	And make my seated heart knock at my ribs?
	If chance will have me King, why, chance may crown me,
	Without my stir.
BANQUO	Look, how our partner's rapt.
	Worthy Macbeth, we stay upon your leisure.
MACBETH	My dull brain was wrought with things forgotten.
	Let us toward the King. *Exeunt Banquo, Ross, and Angus.*
	Stars, hide your fires;
	Let not light see my black and deep desires;
	The eye wink at the hand; yet let that be
	Which the eye fears, when it is done, to see. *Exit.*

Scene 2

The scene shifts now to Macbeth's castle at Inverness. Here Lady Macbeth awaits her lord's return. In a letter Macbeth tells her of his meeting with the witches.

Holinshed wrote that Macbeth was the grandson of King Mal-

127

colm, and was therefore an heir to the throne. *Other historians,
however, say that it was Macbeth's wife Gruoch who was a
member of the royal family, and that his only claim to the
throne was through her. Whatever may have been true of the
historical lady's claim, there is no question of her desire for the
throne. Holinshed says she was "verie ambitious, burning in
unquenchable desire to bear the name of queen."*

*When Lady Macbeth reads her husband's letter she knows im-
mediately how the third witch's prophecy must be fulfilled and
never shrinks from the thought of it; yet she fears that Macbeth
lacks the necessary cruelty to do what must be done. When he
arrives, however, and tells her Duncan is coming to stay with
them this very night, she knows by his face that he is thinking
what she is thinking: here is their opportunity — an opportunity
given to them by Fate — to murder Duncan.*

And so they prepare to welcome their royal guest.

Enter Lady Macbeth, reading a letter.

LADY MACBETH "They met me in the day of success; and I have learn'd that they
have more in them than mortal knowledge. When I burn'd in
desire to question them further, they made themselves air, into
which they vanish'd. Whiles I stood rapt in the wonder of it,
came missives from the King, who all-hail'd me 'Thane of
Cawdor,' by which title, before, these weird sisters saluted me,
and referred me to the coming on of time with 'Hail, King that
shalt be!' This have I thought good to deliver thee, that thou
mightest not be ignorant of what greatness is promis'd thee.
Lay it to thy heart, and farewell."
Glamis thou art, and Cawdor, and shalt be
What thou art promis'd. Yet do I fear thy nature;
It is too full o' th' milk of human kindness
To catch the nearest way. What thou wouldst highly,
That wouldst thou holily; wouldst not play false,
And yet wouldst wrongly win. Hie thee hither,
That I may pour my spirits in thine ear,
And chastise with the valor of my tongue
All that impedes thee from the golden round.
Enter Macbeth.
Great Glamis, worthy Cawdor,
Greater than both, by the all-hail hereafter!
Thy letters have transported me beyond
This ignorant present, and I feel now
The future in the instant.

MACBETH   My dearest love,
            Duncan comes here tonight.
LADY MACBETH   And when goes hence?
MACBETH   Tomorrow, as he purposes.
LADY MACBETH   O, never
            Shall sun that morrow see!
            Your face, my thane, is as a book where men
            May read strange matters. To beguile the time,
            Look like the time; bear welcome in your eye,
            Your hand, your tongue: look like th' innocent flower,
            But be the serpent under 't. He that's coming
            Must be provided for; and you shall put
            This night's great business into my dispatch;
            Which shall to all our nights and days to come
            Give solely sovereign sway and masterdom.
MACBETH   We shall speak further.
LADY MACBETH   Only look up clear;
            To alter favor ever is to fear.
            Leave all the rest to me.   *Exit Macbeth.*
            Hoboyes. Enter the King, Malcolm, Donalbain, Banquo, Len-
            nox, Macduff, Ross, Angus, and Attendants.

DUNCAN   This castle hath a pleasant seat; the air
Nimbly and sweetly recommends itself
Unto our senses. See, our honor'd hostess.
We thank you for your trouble.

LADY MACBETH   All our service,
In every point twice done, and then done double,
Were poor and single business, to contend
Against those honors deep and broad, wherewith
Your majesty loads our house.

DUNCAN   Give me your hand;
Conduct me to mine host: we love him highly.   *Exeunt.*

*Night begins to fall. Torches are lighted. From the banquet hall
comes the music of oboes (hoboyes). Duncan and his faithful
thanes are merry as they celebrate their victories.*

*Hoboyes. Torches. Enter divers Servants with dishes and serv-
ice over the stage. Then enter Macbeth.*

MACBETH   If it were done when 'tis done, then 'twere well
It were done quickly. If th' assassination
Could trammel up the consequence, and catch
With his surcease success: that but this blow
Might be the be-all and the end-all — here,
But here, upon this bank and shoal of time,
We'd jump the life to come. But in these cases
We still have judgment here; that we but teach
Bloody instructions, which being taught, return
To plague th' inventor. This even-handed justice
Commends th' ingredients of our poison'd chalice
To our own lips. He's here in double trust:
First, as I am his kinsman and his subject,
Strong both against the deed; then, as his host,
Who should against his murtherer shut the door,
Not bear the knife myself. Besides, this Duncan
Hath borne his faculties so meek, hath been
So clear in his great office, that his virtues
Will plead like angels, trumpet-tongu'd against
The deep damnation of his taking-off;
And Pity, like a naked new-born babe,
Striding the blast, or heaven's cherubin, hors'd
Upon the sightless couriers of the air,
Shall blow the horrid deed in every eye,
That tears shall drown the wind. I have no spur
To prick the sides of my intent, but only
Vaulting ambition.

Enter Lady Macbeth. How now? What news?

LADY MACBETH   He has almost supp'd. Why have you left the chamber?

MACBETH   We will proceed no further in this business;
He hath honor'd me of late.

LADY MACBETH   Was the hope drunk
Wherein you dress'd yourself? Hath it slept since?
And wakes it now to look so green and pale
At what it did so freely?

MACBETH   Prithee, peace.
I dare do all that may become a man;
Who dares do more is none.

LADY MACBETH   What beast was 't then
That made you break this enterprise to me?
When you durst do it then you were a man.

MACBETH   If we should fail —

LADY MACBETH   We fail?
But screw your courage to the sticking-place,
And we'll not fail. When Duncan is asleep,
His chamberlains will I with wine and wassail
Well convince, and when in swinish sleep
Their drenched natures lie as in a death,
What cannot you and I perform upon
Th' unguarded Duncan?

MACBETH   Will it not be receiv'd
When we have mark'd with blood those sleepy two
Of his own chamber, and used their very daggers,
That they have done 't?

LADY MACBETH   Who dares receive it other,
As we shall make your griefs and clamor roar
Upon his death?

MACBETH   I am settled, and bend up
Each corporal agent to this terrible feat.
Away, and mock the time with fairest show:
False face must hide what the false heart doth know.   *Exeunt.*

Scene 3

*The sounds of music die, and all is quiet. The clock strikes two.
It is the dead, black middle of the night. Yet Banquo cannot
sleep. And there are others who are still awake, who still have
work to do, deeds to perform upon the unguarded Duncan.
Even before the deed is done, Macbeth's conscience is prey to
his guilty fancies. Lady Macbeth, on the other hand, is all steel;
she keeps her wits about her, and remembers all the little details*

that will point suspicion away from them. When they are inter-
rupted by a knocking at the gate, her words of assurance, "A
little water clears us of this deed," strike a terribly ironic note.
Their hands will never be clean again.

Enter Banquo, and Fleance with a Torchbearer before him.

BANQUO	How goes the night, boy?
FLEANCE	The moon is down; I have not heard the clock.
BANQUO	And she goes down at twelve.
FLEANCE	I take 't, 'tis later, sir.
BANQUO	A heavy summons lies like lead upon me.

And yet I would not sleep. Merciful powers,
Restrain in me the cursed thoughts that nature
Gives way to in repose.
Enter Macbeth, and a Servant with a torch.
                    Who's there?

MACBETH   A friend.

BANQUO   What, sir, not yet at rest? The King's a-bed.
I dreamt last night of the three weird sisters:
To you they have show'd some truth.

MACBETH   I think not of them.
Yet, when we can entreat an hour to serve,
We would spend it in some words upon that business,
If you would grant the time.

BANQUO   At your kind'st leisure.

MACBETH   It shall make honor for you.

BANQUO   So I lose none,
I shall be counsel'd.

MACBETH   Good repose the while.

BANQUO   Thanks, sir: the like to you.   *Exeunt Banquo and Fleance.*

MACBETH   Go bid thy mistress, when my drink is ready
She strike upon the bell. Get thee to bed.   *Exit Servant.*
Is this a dagger which I see before me,
The handle toward my hand? Come, let me clutch thee.
I have thee not, and yet I see thee still;
And on thy blade and dudgeon gouts of blood.
There's no such thing. Now o'er the one half world
Nature seems dead, and wicked dreams abuse
The curtain'd sleep; witchcraft celebrates
Pale Hecate's off'rings; and wither'd Murther,
With his stealthy pace, towards his design
Moves like a ghost.
A bell rings.
I go, and it is done; the bell invites me.
Hear it not, Duncan, for it is a knell

	That summons thee to heaven or to hell. *Exit.*
	Enter Lady Macbeth.
LADY MACBETH	That which hath made them drunk hath made me bold:
	Hark! Peace. It was the owl that shriek'd,
	The fatal bellman, which gives the stern'st good night.
MACBETH	*Within.* Who's there? What, ho!
LADY MACBETH	I fear they have awak'd,
	And 'tis not done; th' attempt and not the deed
	Confounds us. Hark! I laid their daggers ready;
	He could not miss 'em. Had he not resembled
	My father as he slept I had done 't. My husband!
	Enter Macbeth.
MACBETH	I have done the deed. Didst thou not hear a noise?
LADY MACBETH	I heard the owl scream and the crickets cry.
MACBETH	Methought I heard a voice cry "Sleep no more!
	Macbeth does murther Sleep," the innocent Sleep,
	Sleep that knits up the ravel'd sleave of care.
	Still it cried, "Sleep no more!" to all the house;
	"Glamis hath murther'd Sleep, and therefore Cawdor
	Shall sleep no more: Macbeth shall sleep no more!"
LADY MACBETH	You do unbend your noble strength to think
	So brainsickly of things. Go get some water,
	And wash this filthy witness from your hand.
	Why did you bring these daggers from the place?
	They must lie there. Go carry them, and smear
	The sleepy grooms with blood.
MACBETH	I'll go no more.
	I am afraid to think what I have done;
	Look on 't again I dare not.
LADY MACBETH	Infirm of purpose!
	Give me the daggers. The sleeping and the dead
	Are but as pictures; 'tis the eye of childhood
	That fears a painted devil. If he do bleed,
	I'll gild the faces of the grooms withal,
	For it must seem their guilt. *Exit Lady Macbeth.*
	A knock within.
MACBETH	Whence is that knocking?
	How is 't with me, when every noise appalls me?
	Will all great Neptune's ocean wash this blood
	Clean from my hand? No, this my hand will rather
	The multitudinous seas incarnadine,
	Making the green one red.
	Enter Lady Macbeth.
LADY MACBETH	My hands are of your color, but I shame
	To wear a heart so white. *Knock.*

133

	I hear a knocking at the south entry.
	Retire we to our chamber.
	A little water clears us of this deed.
	How easy is it then. *Knock.*
	Hark! More knocking.
	Get on your nightgown, lest occasion call us,
	And show us to be watchers. *Knock.*
MACBETH	Wake Duncan with thy knocking!
	I would thou couldst. *Exeunt.*

The servants were carousing until a late hour. The porter, grumbling at being routed out of his warm bed, and still half asleep, is thinking what it would be like if a man were the gateman of hell: then "he would have old turning the key," he says (which means he would have a busy old time unlocking the gate). He pretends that he is greeting newcomers to hell — first a suicide then a thief — until the cold night air makes it impossible to pretend longer that this is hell. Finally he opens the gate.

Yet note the irony here; for this porter who keeps the gate of Macbeth's castle is, in a very literal sense, the keeper of the gate to hell — the hell that Macbeth and Lady Macbeth have created for themselves.

Enter a Porter. More knocking within.

PORTER — Here's a knocking, indeed! If a man were porter of hell-gate he should have old turning the key. *Knock.* Knock, knock, knock! Who's there, i' th' name of Beelzebub? Here's a farmer that hang'd himself. Come in; have napkins enow about you: here you'll sweat for 't. *Knock.* Knock, knock! Who's there, i' th' other devil's name? Faith, here's a tailor come hither for stealing. Come in, tailor; here you may roast your goose. *Knock.* Knock, Knock! Never at quiet. What are you? But this place is too cold for hell. I'll devil-porter it no further. I had thought to have let in some of all professions, that go the primrose way to th' everlasting bonfire. *Knock.* Anon, anon! *Opens the gate. Enter Macduff and Lennox.* I pray you, remember the porter.

MACDUFF — Was it so late, friend, ere you went to bed, that you do lie so late?

PORTER — Faith, sir, we were carousing till the second cock.

MACDUFF — Is thy master stirring?
Enter Macbeth.
Our knocking has awak'd him; here he comes.

135

LENNOX	Good morrow, noble sir.
MACBETH	Good morrow, both.
MACDUFF	Is the King stirring, worthy thane?
MACBETH	Not yet.
MACDUFF	He did command me to call timely on him; I have almost slipp'd the hour.
MACBETH	I'll bring you to him. This is the door.
MACDUFF	I'll make so bold to call. *Exit Macduff.*
LENNOX	Goes the King hence today?
MACBETH	He did appoint so.
LENNOX	The night has been unruly. Where we lay, our chimneys were blown down, And, as they say, lamentings heard i' th' air, Strange screams of death, And prophesying of confus'd events New hatch'd to th' woeful time. The obscure bird clamor'd the livelong night. Some say the earth was feverous, and did shake.
MACBETH	'Twas a rough night. *Enter Macduff.*

136

MACDUFF	O horror, horror, horror!
MACBETH LENNOX	} What's the matter?
MACDUFF	Most sacrilegious murther hath been done.
MACBETH	What is 't you say?
LENNOX	Mean you his Majesty?
MACDUFF	Approach the chamber, and destroy your sight With a new Gorgon. Do not bid me speak. See, and then speak yourselves. *Exeunt Macbeth and Lennox.* Awake! Awake! Ring the alarum-bell. Murther and treason! *Bell rings.* *Enter Lady Macbeth.*
LADY MACBETH	What's the business? Speak!
MACDUFF	O gentle lady, 'Tis not for you to hear what I can speak; *Enter Banquo.* O Banquo, Banquo, our royal master's murther'd!
LADY MACBETH	What, in our house?
BANQUO	Too cruel anywhere. Dear Duff, I prithee contradict thyself, And say it is not so. *Enter Macbeth and Lennox.*
MACBETH	Had I but died an hour before this chance, I had liv'd a blessed time; for grace is dead. *Enter Malcolm, Donalbain, and others.*
DONALBAIN	What is amiss?
MACBETH	You are, and do not know 't: The spring, the head, the fountain of your blood Is stopp'd; the very source of it is stopp'd.
MACDUFF	Your royal father's murther'd.
MALCOLM	O, by whom?
LENNOX	Those of his chamber, as it seem'd, had done 't. Their hands and faces were all badg'd with blood; So were their daggers, which unwip'd we found Upon their pillows.
MACBETH	O, yet I do repent me of my fury, That I did kill them.
MACDUFF	Wherefore did you so?
MACBETH	Who can be wise, amaz'd, temp'rate and furious, Loyal and neutral at once? Who could refrain, That had a heart to love, and in that heart Courage to make 's love known?
LADY MACBETH	Help me hence, ho!

MACDUFF	Look to the lady.
MALCOLM	*Aside to Donalbain.* Why do we hold our tongues?
DONALBAIN	*Aside to Malcolm.* What should be spoken here, where our fate May rush and seize us?
BANQUO	Look to the lady, ho!

Lady Macbeth is carried out.

And when we have our naked frailties hid,
That suffer in exposure, let us meet,
And question this most bloody piece of work,
To know it further.

MACBETH	Put on manly readiness,

And meet i' th' hall together.

ALL	Well contented.

Exeunt all but Malcolm and Donalbain.

MALCOLM	Let's not consort with them. I'll to England.
DONALBAIN	To Ireland, I; our separated fortune

Shall keep us both the safer. Where we are
There's daggers in men's smiles; the near in blood,
The nearer bloody.

MALCOLM	This murtherous shaft that's shot

Hath not yet lighted, and our safest way
Is to avoid the aim. Therefore, to horse!
And let us not be dainty of leave-taking,
But shift away. There's warrant in that theft
Which steals itself when there's no mercy left.   *Exeunt.*

ACT II
———
Scene 1

*The murdered King's two sons Malcolm and Donalbain having
wisely decided to flee, Macbeth as next in line of succession has
won the crown. So ended Act I.*

*Act II will show the lengths to which he must go in order to
keep his ill-gotten crown. The blame for Duncan's murder was
laid on his sons, because they fled. The thanes have accepted
that verdict, but they wonder and they watch. Macbeth fears
Banquo, who knows too much; therefore Banquo must die. So
must Banquo's son, because the witches foretold that Banquo
would be the father of many kings. Macduff suspects Macbeth
and keeps away from him; therefore Macduff must die. And
each new bloody deed adds more weight to the burden on
Macbeth's conscience.*

	Enter Banquo.
BANQUO	Thou hast it now: King, Cawdor, Glamis, all,
	As the weird women promis'd; and I fear
	Thou play'dst most foully for 't; yet it was said
	It should not stand in thy posterity,
	But that myself should be the root and father
	Of many Kings. But hush, no more.

Sennet sounded. Enter Macbeth as King, Lady Macbeth as Queen, Lennox, Ross, Lords, and Attendants.

MACBETH	Tonight we hold a solemn supper, sir.
	And I'll request your presence.
BANQUO	Let your Highness
	Command upon me, to the which my duties
	Are with a most indissoluble tie
	Forever knit.
MACBETH	Ride you this afternoon?
BANQUO	Ay, my good lord.
MACBETH	We should have else desir'd your good advice
	In this day's council; but we'll take tomorrow.
	We hear our bloody cousins are bestow'd
	In England and in Ireland, not confessing
	Their cruel parricide. But of that tomorrow.
	Is 't far you ride?
BANQUO	As far, my lord, as will fill up the time
	'Twixt this and supper.
MACBETH	Do not fail our feast.
BANQUO	My lord, I will not.
MACBETH	Hie you to horse. Adieu,
	Till you return at night. Goes Fleance with you?
BANQUO	Ay, my good lord; our time does call upon 's.
MACBETH	I wish your horses swift and sure of foot;
	And so I do commend you to their backs.
	Farewell. *Exit Banquo.*
	Let every man be master of his time
	Till seven at night.
	While then, God be with you.
	Exeunt all but Macbeth and a Servant.
	Sirrah, a word with you.
	Attend those men our pleasure?
SERVANT	They are, my lord, without the palace gate.
MACBETH	Bring them before us. *Exit Servant.*
	To be thus is nothing, but to be safely thus.
	Our fears in Banquo stick deep,
	And in his royalty of nature reigns
	That which would be fear'd. He chid the sisters

When first they put the name of King upon me,
And bade them speak to him. Then, prophet-like,
They hail'd him father to a line of Kings.
Upon my head they plac'd a fruitless crown,
No son of mine succeeding. If 't be so,
For Banquo's issue have I fil'd my mind;
For them the gracious Duncan have I murther'd!
Enter Servant and two Murtherers.
Now go to the door, and stay there till we call. *Exit Servant.*
Was it not yesterday we spoke together?

MURTHERERS It was, so please your Highness.

MACBETH   Well then,
Have you consider'd of my speech?

SECOND MURTHERER   I am one
Whom the vile blows and buffets of the world
Have so incens'd that I am reckless what
I do to spite the world.

FIRST MURTHERER   And I another,
So weary with disasters, tugg'd with Fortune,
That I would set my life on any chance,
To mend it or be rid on 't.

MACBETH   Both of you
Know Banquo was your enemy.

MURTHERERS	True, my lord.
MACBETH	So is he mine.
SECOND MURTHERER	We shall, my lord,
	Perform what you command us.
MACBETH	It must be done tonight,
	And something from the palace; and with him,
	To leave no rubs nor botches in the work,
	Fleance his son, that keeps him company,
	Must embrace the fate of that dark hour.
	Resolve yourselves.
MURTHERERS	We are resolv'd, my lord.

Exeunt Murtherers.

MACBETH	It is concluded. Come, seeling night,
	Scarf up the tender eye of pitiful day,
	And with thy bloody and invisible hand
	Cancel and tear to pieces that great bond
	Which keeps me pale. Light thickens,
	And the crow makes wings to th' rocky wood.
	Good things of day begin to droop and drowse,
	Whiles night's black agents to their preys do rouse. *Exit.*

Servants enter with table and benches, and prepare a banquet. Hoboyes. Torches. Enter Macbeth, Lady Macbeth, Ross, Lennox, Lords, and Attendants.

MACBETH	You know your own degrees; sit down.
	At first and last, the hearty welcome.
LENNOX	Thanks to your Majesty.

Enter First Murtherer to the door.

MACBETH	Be large in mirth; anon, we'll drink a measure
	The table round. *He approaches the door.*
	There's blood upon thy face.
MURTHERER	'Tis Banquo's, then.
MACBETH	'Tis better thee without than he within.
	Is he dispatch'd?
MURTHERER	My lord, his throat is cut; that I did for him.
MACBETH	Thou art the best o' th' cut-throats.
MURTHERER	Most royal sir — Fleance is 'scap'd.
MACBETH	Then comes my fit again. But Banquo's safe?
MURTHERER	Ay, my good lord; safe in a ditch he bides.
MACBETH	Thanks for that. Now get thee gone. *Exit Murtherer.*
LADY MACBETH	My lord,
	You do not give the cheer.
MACBETH	Sweet remembrancer!
	Now good digestion wait on appetite,
	And health on both.

Enter the Ghost of Banquo, and sits in Macbeth's place.

LENNOX	May 't please your Highness sit?
MACBETH	Here had we now our country's honor roof'd,
	Were our Banquo present.
ROSS	His absence, sir,
	Lays blame upon his promise. Please 't your Highness
	To grace us with your royal company?
MACBETH	The table's full.
LENNOX	Here is a place reserv'd, sir.
MACBETH	Where?
LENNOX	Here, my good lord.
	What is 't that moves your Highness?
MACBETH	Which of you have done this?
LORDS	What, my good lord?
MACBETH	Thou canst not say I did it; never shake
	Thy gory locks at me.
ROSS	Gentlemen, rise; his Highness is not well.
LADY MACBETH	Sit, worthy friends. My lord is often thus,
	And hath been from his youth. Pray you, keep seat;
	The fit is momentary. *Aside.* Are you a man?
MACBETH	Ay, and a bold one, that dare look on that
	Which might appall the devil.
LADY MACBETH	O proper stuff!
	This is the very painting of your fear.
MACBETH	Prithee, see there! *Exit Ghost*
LADY MACBETH	What! Quite unmann'd in folly?
MACBETH	If I stand here, I saw him.
LADY MACBETH	Fie, for shame.
MACBETH	Blood hath been shed ere now. The time has been,
	That, when the brains were out, the man would die,
	And there an end. But now they rise again,
	And push us from our stools.
LADY MACBETH	My worthy lord,
	Your noble friends do lack you.
MACBETH	I do forget.
	Do not muse at me, my most worthy friends;
	I have a strange infirmity, which is nothing
	To those that know me. Come, love and health to all,
	And to our dear friend Banquo, whom we miss.
	Would he were here.
	Enter Ghost.
LORDS	Our duties, and the pledge.
MACBETH	Avaunt, and quit my sight! Let the earth hide thee!
	Thy bones are marrowless, thy blood is cold;
	Thou hast no speculation in those eyes
	Which thou dost glare with.

LADY MACBETH	Think of this, good peers,
	But as a thing of custom. 'Tis no other;
	Only it spoils the pleasure of the time.
MACBETH	What man dare, I dare. Hence, horrible shadow!
	Unreal mock'ry, hence! *Exit Ghost.*
	Why, so; being gone
	I am a man again. Pray you, sit still.
LADY MACBETH	You have displac'd the mirth, broke the good meeting,
	With most admir'd disorder.
MACBETH	Can such things be
	And overcome us like a summer's cloud,
	Without our special wonder? You make me strange
	When now I think you can behold such sights,
	And keep the natural ruby of your cheeks,
	When mine is blanch'd with fear.
ROSS	What sights, my lord?
LADY MACBETH	I pray you, speak not. He grows worse and worse;
	Question enrages him. At once, good night.
	Stand not upon the order of your going,
	But go at once.
LENNOX	Good night; and better health
	Attend his Majesty.

LADY MACBETH	A kind good night to all.
	Exeunt Lords and Attendants.
MACBETH	Blood will have blood, they say. What is the night?
LADY MACBETH	Almost at odds with morning, which is which.
MACBETH	How sayst thou, that Macduff denies his person
	At our great bidding?
LADY MACBETH	Did you send to him, sir?
MACBETH	I did; and with an absolute "Sir, not I"
	He answered. I will to the weird sisters.
	More shall they speak; for now I am bent to know,
	By the worst means, the worst. I am in blood
	Stepp'd in so far that, should I wade no more,
	Returning were as tedious as go o'er.
	Strange things I have in head that will to hand,
	Which must be acted ere they may be scann'd. *Exeunt.*

Scene 2

Macbeth now seeks out the witches, who before had come to him. He desperately wants to know what the future holds. Before he can ask, they answer, and the things they say make him feel invincible. When he demands more — demands to know if Banquo's descendants will ever rule in Scotland — the things they show him fill him with despair.

Shakespeare may have been prompted to write Macbeth *as a subtle compliment to England's new King, James I, who succeeded to the throne in 1603. James, who had been James VI of Scotland, was a distant descendant of Banquo. Furthermore, he was an authority on witchcraft. In 1597 he had published a book entitled* Daemonologie *in which he outlined Christian beliefs about witchcraft.*

	Thunder. Enter the three Witches.
FIRST WITCH	Thrice the brinded cat hath mew'd.
SECOND WITCH	Thrice, and once the hedge-pig whin'd.
THIRD WITCH	Harpier cries; 'tis time, 'tis time.
FIRST WITCH	Round about the cauldron go;
	In the poison'd entrails throw.
ALL THREE	Double, double, toil, and trouble;
	Fire burn, and cauldron bubble.
SECOND WITCH	Eye of newt, and toe of frog,
	Wool of bat, and tongue of dog,

144

	Adder's fork, and blindworm's sting,
	Lizard's leg, and howlet's wing.
ALL THREE	Double, double, toil, and trouble;
	Fire burn, and cauldron bubble.
THIRD WITCH	Scale of dragon, tooth of wolf,
	Witches' mummy, maw and gulf
	Of the ravin'd salt-sea shark;
	Root of hemlock digg'd i' th' dark.
ALL THREE	Double, double, toil, and trouble;
	Fire burn, and cauldron bubble.
FIRST WITCH	Cool it with a baboon's blood,
	Then the charm is firm and good.
SECOND WITCH	By the pricking of my thumbs,
	Something wicked this way comes.
	Open, locks, whoever knocks.
	Enter Macbeth.
MACBETH	How now, you secret, black, and midnight hags?
	What is 't you do?
ALL THREE	A deed without a name.
MACBETH	I conjure you, by that which you profess —
	Howe'er you come to know it — answer me
	To what I ask of you.
ALL THREE	We know thy thought:
	Hear our speech, but say thou nought.
FIRST WITCH	Macbeth! Macbeth! Macbeth! Beware Macduff.
MACBETH	Thou hast harp'd my fear aright. But one word more —
FIRST WITCH	We will not be commanded.
SECOND WITCH	Macbeth! Macbeth! Macbeth!
	Be bloody, bold, and resolute; laugh to scorn
	The power of man; for none of woman born
	Shall harm Macbeth.
MACBETH	Then live, Macduff; what need I fear of thee?
	But yet I'll make assurance double sure,
	And take a bond of fate. Thou shalt not live;
	That I may tell pale-hearted fear it lies,
	And sleep in spite of thunder. What of you?
THIRD WITCH	Be lion-mettled, proud, and take no care
	Who chafes, who frets, or where conspirers are.
	Macbeth shall never vanquish'd be until
	Great Birnam wood to high Dunsinane hill
	Shall come against him.
MACBETH	That will never be:
	Who can impress the forest, bid the tree
	Unfix his earthbound root? Tell, if your art
	Can tell so much: shall Banquo's issue ever

	Reign in this kingdom?
ALL THREE	Seek to know no more.
MACBETH	I will be satisfied. Deny me this,
	And an eternal curse fall on you! Let me know.
	Sound of hoboyes.
FIRST WITCH	Show!
SECOND WITCH	Show!
THIRD WITCH	Show!
ALL THREE	Show his eyes, and grieve his heart;
	Come like shadows, so depart.
	A show of eight Kings and Banquo; the last King carries a glass in his hand.
MACBETH	Thou art too like the spirit of Banquo; down!
	Thy crown does sear mine eyeballs like the first.
	A third is like the former. — A fourth? Start, eyes!
	What, will the line stretch out to th' crack of doom?
	Another yet? A seventh? I'll see no more.
	And yet the eighth appears, who bears a glass
	Which shows me many more. I see, 'tis true,
	For the blood-bolter'd Banquo smiles upon me,
	And points at them for his. What? Is this so?
	The Apparitions vanish.
FIRST WITCH	Ay, sir, all this is so.
	The Witches vanish.
MACBETH	Where are they? Gone? Let this pernicious hour
	Stand aye accursed in the calendar!
	Come in, without there!
	Enter Lennox.
LENNOX	What's your Grace's will?
MACBETH	Saw you the weird sisters?
LENNOX	No, my lord.
MACBETH	Came they not by you?
LENNOX	No indeed, my lord.
MACBETH	Infected be the air whereon they ride,
	And damn'd all those that trust them! I did hear
	The galloping of horse: who was 't came by?
LENNOX	'Tis two or three, my lord, that bring you word
	Macduff is fled to England.
MACBETH	Fled to England?
LENNOX	Ay, my good lord.
MACBETH	Time, thou anticipat'st my dread exploits.
	From this moment be it thought and done:
	The very firstlings of my heart shall be
	The firstlings of my hand. And even now
	The castle of Macduff I will surprise,

Seize upon Fife, give to th' edge o' th' sword
His wife, his babes, and all unfortunate souls
That trace him in his line. No boasting like a fool;
This deed I'll do before the purpose cool. *Exeunt.*

ACT III
—
Scene 1

*In Act I Macbeth killed to get the crown. In Act II he killed
to keep it. Act III brings retribution.*

*Malcolm, the rightful heir to the throne, sought refuge in Eng-
land when his father was murdered. Here he has been waiting
until the Scottish lords should be ready to rise in his support
against the usurper, and here he has been joined by Macduff.
When Ross comes, too, bringing word of the cruel slaughter of
Macduff's family, they resolve to wait no longer but to march
at once against Macbeth.*

Enter Malcolm and Macduff.

MALCOLM   Let us seek out some desolate shade, and there
Weep our sad bosoms empty.

MACDUFF   O Scotland, Scotland!
With an untitled tyrant bloody-scepter'd.
When shalt thou see thy wholesome days again?

MALCOLM   I think our country sinks beneath the yoke;
It weeps, it bleeds, and each new day a gash
Is added to her wounds. I think withal,
There would be hands uplifted in my right;
And here from gracious England have I offer
Of good Siward and ten thousand warlike men.
Enter Ross.

MACDUFF   See who comes here.

MALCOLM   It is my countryman.

MACDUFF   My ever-gentle cousin, welcome hither.
Stands Scotland where it did?

ROSS   Alas, poor country,
Almost afraid to know itself. It cannot
Be call'd our mother, but our grave.

MALCOLM   What's the newest grief?

ROSS   I have words
That would be howl'd out in the desert air,
Where hearing should not latch them.

MACDUFF   What concern they?

147

ROSS	No mind that's honest but in it shares some woe,
	Though the main part pertains to you alone.
MACDUFF	Keep it not from me; quickly let me have it.
ROSS	Let not your ears despise my tongue forever.
	Your castle is surpris'd; your wife and babes
	Savagely slaughter'd. To relate the manner
	Would add the death of you.
MALCOLM	Merciful heaven!
	Give sorrow words; the grief that does not speak
	Whispers the o'er-fraught heart and bids it break.
MACDUFF	My children too?
ROSS	Wife, children, servants, all that could be found.
MACDUFF	And I must be from thence! My wife kill'd too?
ROSS	I have said.
MALCOLM	Be comforted.
	Let's make us med'cines of our great revenge,
	To cure this deadly grief.
MACDUFF	He has no children. All my pretty ones?
	Did you say all? O hell-kite! All?
	At one fell swoop?
MALCOLM	Dispute it like a man.
MACDUFF	I shall do so;
	But I must also feel it as a man.
	Did heaven look on, and would not take their part?
MALCOLM	Be this the whetstone of your sword; let grief
	Convert to anger.
MACDUFF	Front to front
	Bring thou this fiend of Scotland and myself;
	Within my sword's length set him; if he scape,
	Heaven forgive him too.
MALCOLM	This tune goes manly.
	Come, go we to the King; our power is ready;
	Our lack is nothing but our leave. Macbeth
	Is ripe for shaking. Receive what cheer you may;
	The night is long that never finds the day. *Exeunt.*

Scene 2

The action in this last long scene is essentially continuous. There will be pauses, like the pauses after points in a game of tennis. Attention will shift back and forth between the antagonists, as in tennis. Nevertheless, the scene is a single dramatic unit, as a tennis game is a unit — and Macbeth loses almost every point.

First, attention is drawn to Lady Macbeth, a pathetic shadow of the once indomitable lady, now living in a perpetual nightmare. Hear in her agonized cry "Will these hands ne'er be clean?" the echo of her earlier words, "A little water clears us of this deed." And pity her.

Enter a Doctor and a Waiting Gentlewoman.

DOCTOR I have two nights watch'd with you, but can perceive no truth in your report. When was it she last walk'd?

GENTLEWOMAN Lo you, here she comes.
Enter Lady Macbeth.
This is her very guise, and upon my life, fast asleep. Observe her; stand close.

DOCTOR You see her eyes are open.

GENTLEWOMAN Ay, but their sense is shut.

DOCTOR What is it she does now? Look how she rubs her hands.

GENTLEWOMAN It is an accustom'd action with her, to seem thus washing her hands. I have known her continue in this a quarter of an hour.

LADY MACBETH Yet here's a spot.

DOCTOR Hark, she speaks.

LADY MACBETH Out, damned spot! Out, I say! One; two. Why, then, 'tis time to do 't. Hell is murky. Fie, my lord, fie! A soldier, and afraid? Yet who would have thought the old man to have had so much blood in him?

DOCTOR Do you mark that?

LADY MACBETH The Thane of Fife had a wife. Where is she now? What, will

	these hands ne'er be clean? Here's the smell of the blood still. All the perfumes of Arabia will not sweeten this little hand. Oh, oh, oh!
DOCTOR	What a sigh is there! The heart is sorely charg'd.
GENTLEWOMAN	I would not have such a heart in my bosom for the dignity of the whole body.
LADY MACBETH	Wash your hands, look not so pale. I tell you yet again, Banquo's buried; he cannot come out on 's grave.
DOCTOR	Even so?
LADY MACBETH	To bed, to bed: there's knocking at the gate. Come, come, come, come, give me your hand. What's done cannot be undone. To bed, to bed, to bed. *Exit.*
DOCTOR	Will she go now to bed?
GENTLEWOMAN	Directly.
DOCTOR	More needs she the divine than the physician. God, God forgive us all. Look after her; Remove from her the means of all annoyance, And still keep eyes upon her. So, good night. My mind she has mated, and amaz'd my sight. I think, but dare not speak.
GENTLEWOMAN	Good night, good doctor. *Exeunt.*

Look away from Dunsinane for a moment and see the Scottish thanes abandoning Macbeth to go to Malcolm. Then back to Dunsinane, and hear Macbeth's angry retort when he learns of their desertion, "Then fly, false thanes. . . . I will not be afraid of death and bane till Birnam forest come to Dunsinane." Immediately after that boast, see Malcolm at Birnam wood ordering his soldiers to cut branches from the trees and carry them as camouflage.

Enter Menteth, Cathness, Angus, Lennox, Soldiers.

MENTETH	The English power is near, led on by Malcolm, His uncle Siward, and the good Macduff. Revenges burn in them.
ANGUS	Near Birnam wood Shall we well meet with them.
MENTETH	What does the tyrant?
CATHNESS	Great Dunsinane he strongly fortifies. Some say he's mad; others that lesser hate him Do call it valiant fury.
ANGUS	Now does he feel His secret murthers sticking on his hands. Those he commands move only in command, Nothing in love.

150

CATHNESS   Well, march we on,
               To give obedience where 'tis truly ow'd.   *Exeunt.*
               Enter Macbeth, Doctor, and Attendants.
MACBETH   Bring me no more reports; let them fly all!
               Till Birnam wood remove to Dunsinane
               I cannot taint with fear. What's the boy Malcolm?
               Was he not born of woman? The spirits have said
               "Fear not, Macbeth; no man that's born of woman
               Shall e'er have power upon thee." Then fly, false thanes!
               Enter a Servant.
               The devil damn thee black, thou cream-fac'd loon!
               Where got'st thou that goose look?
SERVANT   There is ten thousand —
MACBETH   Geese, villain?
SERVANT   Soldiers, sir.
MACBETH   Thou lily-liver'd boy. What soldiers, wheyface?
SERVANT   The English force, so please you.
MACBETH   Take thy face hence.   *Exit Servant.*
                                    I am sick at heart. This push
               Will cheer me ever or disseat me now.
               I have liv'd long enough. My way of life
               Is fall'n into the sere, the yellow leaf;
               And that which should accompany old age,
               As honor, love, obedience, troops of friends,
               I must not look to have; but in their stead,
               Curses, not loud but deep.
               How does your patient, doctor?
DOCTOR   Not so sick, my lord,
               As she is troubled with thick-coming fancies
               That keep her from her rest.
MACBETH   Cure her of that!
               Canst thou not minister to a mind diseas'd,
               Pluck from the memory a rooted sorrow
               Which weighs upon the heart?
DOCTOR   Therein the patient
               Must minister to himself.
MACBETH   Throw physic to the dogs; I'll none of it.
               Come, put mine armor on. Give me my staff.
               I will not be afraid of death and bane.
               Till Birnam forest come to Dunsinane.   *Exeunt.*
               *Drum and colors. Enter Malcolm, Siward, Macduff, Siward's
               son, Menteth, Angus, Lennox, Ross, and Soldiers, marching.*
SIWARD   What wood is this before us?
MENTETH   The wood of Birnam.
MALCOLM   Let every soldier hew him down a bough

	And bear 't before him: thereby shall we shadow
	The numbers of our host, and make discovery
	Err in report of us.
SOLDIER	It shall be done.
SIWARD	We learn no other but the confident tyrant
	Keeps still in Dunsinane, and will endure
	Our setting down before 't.
MALCOLM	'Tis his main hope;
	For none serve with him but constrained things
	Whose hearts are absent too.
SIWARD	The time approaches
	That will with due decision make us know
	What we shall say we have and what we owe. *Exeunt marching.*

Now turn once more to Dunsinane. Firmly entrenched in his castle, and protected by the witches' promises, Macbeth is ready for the siege. Before he faces his enemy, however, his heart (and he has a heart) must be broken: he learns that Lady Macbeth is dead. Yet even that is not all he has to bear. His courage, too, must be broken. One of the witches' two promises on which he has literally bet his life is proved to be false — false in its meaning to him, although still true in words.

Enter Macbeth, Seyton, and Soldiers, with drum and colors.

MACBETH	Hang out our banners on the outward walls.
	The cry is still, "They come!" Our castle's strength
	Will laugh a siege to scorn. Here let them lie
	Till famine and the ague eat them up.
	From within, a cry of women.
	What is that noise?
SEYTON	It is the cry of women, my good lord. *Exit.*
MACBETH	I have almost forgot the taste of fears.
	The time has been, my senses would have cool'd
	To hear a night-shriek. I have supp'd full with horrors.
	Enter Seyton.
	Wherefore was that cry?
SEYTON	The Queen, my lord, is dead.
MACBETH	She should have died hereafter;
	There would have been a time for such a word.
	Tomorrow, and tomorrow, and tomorrow,
	Creeps in this petty pace from day to day,
	To the last syllable of recorded time;
	And all our yesterdays have lighted fools
	The way to dusty death. Out, out, brief candle.
	Life's but a walking shadow, a poor player

That struts and frets his hour upon the stage,
And then is heard no more. It is a tale
Told by an idiot, full of sound and fury,
Signifying nothing.
Enter a Messenger.
Thou com'st to use thy tongue; thy story quickly.

MESSENGER Gracious my lord,
I should report that which I say I saw,
But know not how to do't.

MACBETH   Well, say, sir.

MESSENGER As I did stand my watch upon the hill,
I look'd toward Birnam, and anon, methought,
The wood began to move.

MACBETH   Liar and slave!

MESSENGER Let me endure your wrath if 't be not so:
Within this three mile may you see it coming;
I say, a moving grove.

MACBETH   If thou speak'st false,
Upon the next tree shalt thou hang alive
Till famine cling thee. If thy speech be sooth,
I care not if thou dost for me as much.
I pull in resolution and begin
To doubt th' equivocation of the fiend
That lies like truth. "Fear not, till Birnam wood
Do come to Dunsinane," and now a wood
Comes toward Dunsinane. Arm, arm, and out!
Ring the alarum bell! Blow, wind! Come, wrack!
At least we'll die with harness on our back.   *Exeunt.*

*Malcolm and his army storm the castle. The battle rages
around the castle walls. The alarum bell clangs, trumpets blast,
sword rings against sword, men run here and there pursued or
pursuing. In the midst of the battle there is a momentary
glimpse of Macbeth. He feels now like the bear chained to the
post and attacked by dogs in the cruel sport called bearbaiting.*

*Drum and colors. Enter Malcolm, Siward, Macduff, and their
Army, with boughs.*

MALCOLM Now near enough; your leavy screens throw down,
And show like those you are. You, worthy uncle,
Shall with my cousin, your right-noble son,
Lead our first battle.

SIWARD   Fare you well.
Do we but find the tyrant's power tonight,
Let us be beaten, if we cannot fight.

153

MACDUFF	Make all our trumpets speak; give them all breath,
	Those clamorous harbingers of blood and death! *Exeunt.*
	Alarums continued. Enter Macbeth.
MACBETH	They have tied me to a stake; I cannot fly,
	But bearlike I must fight the course. What's he
	That was not born of woman? Such a one
	Am I to fear, or none.
	Enter Young Siward.
YOUNG SIWARD	What is thy name?
MACBETH	Thou'lt be afraid to hear it.
YOUNG SIWARD	No; though thou call'st thyself a hotter name
	Than any is in hell.
MACBETH	My name's Macbeth.
YOUNG SIWARD	The devil himself could not pronounce a title
	More hateful to mine ear.
MACBETH	No, nor more fearful.
YOUNG SIWARD	Thou liest, abhorred tyrant; with my sword
	I'll prove the lie thou speak'st.
	They fight; Young Siward is slain.
MACBETH	Thou wast born of woman;
	But swords I smile at, weapons laugh to scorn,

Brandish'd by man that's of a woman born.   *Exit.*

All the while Macduff is searching. Searching for Macbeth. When he finds him, Macbeth shows a last glimmer of human pity. He warns Macduff of certain death if he fights against a man whose life is charmed. But Macduff tells Macbeth that his charm is worthless, for he, Macduff, was not born to his mother in the normal way. Macbeth's last hope, the witches' one remaining promise, is thus proved false. In his final despair Macbeth rallies what courage he can and fights on, hopelessly.

Alarums. Enter Macduff.

MACDUFF   That way the noise is. Tyrant, show thy face!
If thou be'st slain and with no stroke of mine,
My wife and children's ghosts will haunt me still.
Let me find him, fortune, and more I beg not.   *Exit.*
Alarum. Enter Macbeth.

MACBETH   Why should I play the Roman fool, and die
On mine own sword? Whiles I see lives, the gashes
Do better upon them.
Enter Macduff.

MACDUFF   Turn, hell-hound, turn!

MACBETH   Of all men else I have avoided thee.
But get thee back, my soul is too much charg'd
With blood of thine already.

MACDUFF   I have no words;
My voice is in my sword, thou bloodier villain
Than terms can give thee out!
They fight. Alarum.

MACBETH   Thou losest labor.
I bear a charmed life, which must not yield
To one of woman born.

MACDUFF   Despair thy charm;
And let the angel whom thou still hast serv'd
Tell thee, Macduff was from his mother's womb
Untimely ripp'd.

MACBETH   Accursed be that tongue that tells me so!
And be these juggling fiends no more believ'd,
That palter with us in a double sense;
That keep the word of promise to our ear,
And break it to our hope. I'll not fight with thee.

MACDUFF   Then yield thee, coward,
And live to be the show and gaze o' the time.
We'll have thee, as our rarer monsters are,
Painted upon a pole, and underwrit,

"Here may you see the tyrant."

MACBETH   I will not yield,
To kiss the ground before young Malcolm's feet,
And to be baited with the rabble's curse.
Though Birnam wood be come to Dunsinane,
And thou oppos'd, being of no woman born,
Yet I will try the last. Lay on, Macduff,
And damn'd be him that first cries, "Hold, enough!"

Exeunt fighting.

Flourish. Enter, with drum and colors, Malcolm, Siward, Ross,
Thanes, and Soldiers.

SIWARD   This way, my lord; the castle's gently render'd;
The day almost itself professes yours,
And little is to do.

MALCOLM   We have met with foes
That strike beside us.

SIWARD   Enter, sir, the castle.

MALCOLM   I would the friends we miss were safe arriv'd.
Macduff is missing, and your noble son.

ROSS   Your son, my lord, has paid a soldier's debt.
He only liv'd but till he was a man,
But like a man he died.

SIWARD   Then he is dead?

ROSS   Ay, my lord.

SIWARD   Had he his hurts before?

ROSS   Ay, on the front.

SIWARD   Why then, God's soldier be he!
Had I as many sons as I have hairs,
I would not wish them to a fairer death;
And so, his knell is knoll'd. Here comes newer comfort.
Enter Macduff.

MACDUFF   Hail, King! For so thou art. Behold, where lies
Th' usurper's cursed head; the time is free.
Hail, King of Scotland!

ALL   Hail, King of Scotland!   *Flourish.*

MALCOLM   My thanks to all at once and to each one.
We shall not spend a large expense of time
Before we reckon with your several loves,
And make us even with you. What's more to do —
As calling home our exil'd friends abroad
That fled the snares of watchful tyranny —
This, and what needful else, by the grace of Grace
We will perform in measure, time, and place.

Flourish. Exeunt omnes.

5

The Tragedy of Julius Caesar

Doors That Books Open

5

AT THE END of the sixteenth century, England was half medieval and half modern. It was still looking backward into the Dark Ages as well as forward toward a brave new world. People were excited by the wonderful new things that were being discovered about their world, by scientists as well as by explorers. That was the time of Copernicus, who took the earth out of the center of the universe and sent it spinning about the sun. It was the time of Tycho Brahe and Galileo and Kepler the star-gazers, of Mercator the mapmaker, of William Harvey, who plotted the course of that important red river the bloodstream. It was the time of Vesalius, who discovered the human body; he explored with his scalpel and identified precisely every bone, every muscle, every organ. At such a time, when men were hungry for knowledge about everything, the schools of England were hopelessly out of date. They taught no mathematics, no science, no history, no geography — in short, they taught almost nothing but Latin, just as schools had been doing all during the Middle Ages.

The Middle Ages had ended, however, whether anyone noticed it at the time or not, somewhere around the middle of the fifteenth century, when Johann Gutenberg invented printing. Until then a book had been a rare and precious item, available only to the very rich, for every word of every copy of every book had to be copied by hand, slowly, painfully. By the middle of the sixteenth century, a hundred years later, there were books — printed books — for even the growing middle classes to read. And it was from books that the Englishman received his real education.

What were the books that a man of Shakespeare's time probably read? In his grammar-school days he read the Latin (and perhaps Greek) classics. From these he learned about Greek and Roman history and mythology. But what else did an Englishman read? What was there in his own language?

Fortunately there was a great flood of new books of all kinds in English. Even though Latin was the language still used for most scientific and scholarly works, some scientists were beginning to write in English. Sir Francis Bacon wrote on law, philosophy, and natural science in English as well as in Latin.

THE UNIVERSE

According to Copernicus

"In the center of everything the sun must reside; in the most beautiful temple created by God, there is the place which awaits him where he can give light to all the planets."

Copernicus

In 1576 Thomas Digges, an English astronomer and mathematician, described the revolutionary new Copernican theory of the universe in English, in his *Perfit Description of the Caelestiall Orbes.*

There were books, pamphlets, and ballads on news events, explorations, discoveries, and politics, for Londoners were eager to know what was going on in the world about them. Sir Walter Raleigh wrote a book called *The Discoverie . . . of Guiana* in which he told about exploring the coast of South America. Captain John Smith wrote about the travels and adventures he had in Europe, Asia, Africa, and America.

People were equally interested in things that had happened in the past. They read with great gusto the stirring story of England's glorious history in Holinshed's *Chronicles* of the history of England, Scotland, and Ireland, which appeared in the 1570's and 1580's.

Their hunger to read and know everything led them to translations of the literature of other languages. And their taste ran from Chapman's translations of Homer's *Iliad* and *Odyssey* to light Italian stories of romantic love and adventure and tragic death. Anything from Italy was very much in fashion just then.

158

These Englishmen who were so eager to read everything, so burning with desire to learn, were the same people who flocked to the theaters; they took their education wherever they could find it. Then as now, playwrights turned the books they read into plays, and any book was meat for the theater's mills — fiction, history, travel, biography. Even science. In one of his plays Shakespeare made an impassioned plea for the medieval conception of the universe; although he may have read about Copernicus's new theory that the earth revolves around the sun, he was certainly not convinced.

The book of greatest interest here, however, was an English translation of Plutarch's *Lives of the Noble Grecians and Romans,* published in 1579. The book was originally written not long after A.D. 100. In it Plutarch told the stories of the lives of Julius Caesar, Brutus, and Mark Antony, and it was on these biographies that Shakespeare based his *Julius Caesar.* In the play he follows very closely the events described by Plutarch. Everything that happens appears first in Plutarch, even relatively insignificant events.

Many times Shakespeare takes actual speeches from Plutarch, touches them with his own special magic, and puts them into the mouths of his characters. Compare two speeches about Cassius.

Plutarch:

"As for those fat men and smooth-combed heads, I never reckon of them: but these pale-visaged and carrion lean people, I fear them most."

Shakespeare:

"Let me have men about me that are fat,

Sleek-headed men, and such as sleep a-nights.

Yond Cassius has a lean and hungry look,

He thinks too much: such men are dangerous."

In this play Shakespeare was attempting to be true to history, to present a study of the evils of tyranny as it had actually been experienced by the Romans of 44 B.C. Even his portrayals of the characters of Caesar and Brutus are similar to Plutarch's.

Despite the fact that the events are historically accurate, however, it is Shakespeare's England that fills in the background. When he wanted to breathe life into these historic characters, Shakespeare took the people of London as his models. The cobbler in the first scene would be completely at home in a London tavern. The battle scenes are like those in the plays Shakespeare wrote about the Kings of England. And the striking of the clock in the scene at Brutus's house may have been perfectly natural in Shakespeare's London — but clocks were not invented until more than a thousand years after Julius Caesar was dead.

Of all Shakespeare's plays, this one, written at the very end of the sixteenth century about events that took place two thousand years ago, is the one that speaks most directly, most pertinently, to today's audience. It is primarily a study of the conflict between expediency and morality. Brutus was an honorable man who made the mistake of fighting tyranny with tyranny's own weapons — assassination, and overthrow of the established government by force. By his action Brutus was partially responsible for the fall of Roman republicanism. He brought to his beloved Rome and her people not "Peace, freedom, and liberty," as he had hoped, but war and new tyranny. What irony in the words of Cassius:

"How many ages hence
Shall this our lofty scene be acted over,
In states unborn and accents yet unknown!

. . . .

So often shall the knot of us be call'd
The men that gave their country liberty."

After Caesar's death the government did not fall into the hands of the people as Brutus had hoped. Instead it was seized by a three-man coalition. This triumvirate, made up of Octavius Caesar, Antony, and Lepidus, eventually gave place to another dictatorship — another Caesar — just as the first triumvirate, made up of Julius Caesar, Pompey, and Crassus, had broken up to leave the first Caesar in sole command.

There is much to ponder in *Julius Caesar*.

The Tragedy of Julius Caesar

5

The Characters:

JULIUS CAESAR
OCTAVIUS CAESAR ⎫
MARK ANTONY ⎬ triumvirs after the death of Julius Caesar
LEPIDUS ⎭
CICERO ⎫
PUBLIUS ⎭ senators
MARCUS BRUTUS ⎫
CAIUS CASSIUS ⎪
CASCA ⎪
TREBONIUS ⎬ conspirators against Julius Caesar
DECIUS BRUTUS ⎪
METELLUS CIMBER ⎪
CINNA ⎭
FLAVIUS ⎫
MARULLUS ⎭ tribunes
ARTEMIDORUS, a Sophist of Cnidos
A SOOTHSAYER
CINNA, a poet
LUCILIUS ⎫
TITINIUS ⎪
MESSALA ⎬ friends of Brutus and Cassius
YOUNG CATO ⎪
VOLUMNIUS ⎭
LUCIUS ⎫
CLITUS ⎪
STRATO ⎬ servants of Brutus
DARDANIUS ⎭
PINDARUS, servant of Cassius
CALPURNIA, wife to Caesar
PORTIA, wife to Brutus
COMMONERS, OR PLEBEIANS, OF ROME; SENATORS, ATTENDANTS, SERVANTS

ACT I

Scene 1

*In the first scene the people of Rome are on a holiday, cele-
brating two things: a Triumph for Caesar and the Feast of
Lupercal.*

*The Feast of Lupercal was a religious festival. Plutarch de-
scribed it this way: "In old time men say it was the feast of
shepherds or herdmen. That day there are divers noblemen's
sons, young men, which run naked through the city, striking in
sport them they meet in their way with leather thongs, hair and
all on." What meaning this ceremony may have had originally
seems to have been forgotten by the time of Julius Caesar. Perhaps it was to protect flocks from wolves (lupus is the Latin
word for wolf), or it may have been a kind of purification rite
to drive away demons and evil spirits. The priests in charge of
the ceremony were called Luperci, and were divided into two
groups, or colleges. In 44 B.C., the year of Caesar's death, a
third college of priests was instituted in honor of Julius Caesar;
Mark Antony was the new group's first magister. When, in this
scene, Cassius says of Caesar "This man is now become a god,"
he may have been speaking the literal truth.*

*The other thing being celebrated is Caesar's Triumph. A Tri-
umph was the highest military honor given in Rome. This one
is in honor of Caesar's victory over Pompey's sons, which ended
the civil wars and established Caesar as sole ruler of the Roman
Republic.*

*In the triumphal procession are musicians, dancers, animals for
sacrifice, and various public officials. In this particular procession there are young men stripped for the race in celebration of
Lupercal (Mark Antony is one of these runners). Then comes
the Imperator, Julius Caesar, holding his scepter with its golden
eagle. When Caesar appears, the crowd greets him with the
shout, "Io Triumphe!"*

In the crowd is a cobbler, an impudent fellow who enjoys bad puns. Notice, for example, the way he plays with the two meanings of "out" (to be angry, and to have worn-out shoes). And why does he choose the word "soles" rather than "shoes," when he describes his trade: "a trade," he says, that he can "use with a safe conscience"?

Not everyone in the crowd is enjoying the holiday. Two tribunes, Marullus and Flavius, hate Caesar for overthrowing Pompey. Cassius is envious of Caesar's power. And Brutus fears that Caesar may yield to the temptation to become a king.

Enter Flavius, Marullus, and certain Commoners.

FLAVIUS   Hence! Home, you idle creatures, get you home.
Is this a holiday? What trade art thou?

COBBLER   A trade, sir, that I hope I may use with a safe conscience, which is indeed, sir, a mender of bad soles.

FLAVIUS   What trade, thou knave? Thou naughty knave, what trade?

COBBLER   Nay, I beseech you, sir, be not out with me: yet, if you be out, sir, I can mend you.

MARULLUS   Mend me, thou saucy fellow?

COBBLER   Why, sir, cobble you.

FLAVIUS   Thou art a cobbler, art thou?

COBBLER   I am indeed, sir, a surgeon to old shoes.

FLAVIUS   But wherefore art not in thy shop today?
Why dost thou lead these men about the streets?

COBBLER   Truly, sir, to wear out their shoes, to get myself into more work.
But, indeed, sir, we make holiday to see Caesar and to rejoice in his Triumph.

MARULLUS   Wherefore rejoice? What conquest brings he home?
You blocks, you stones, you worse than senseless things!
O you hard hearts, you cruel men of Rome,
Knew you not Pompey? Many a time and oft
Have you climb'd up to walls and battlements,
To towers and windows, yea, to chimney tops,
Your infants in your arms, and there have sat
The livelong day, to see great Pompey pass.
And do you now put on your best attire?
And do you now cull out a holiday?
And do you now strew flowers in his way,
That comes in triumph over Pompey's blood?
Be gone!
Run to your houses, fall upon your knees,
Pray to the gods to intermit the plague
That needs must light on this ingratitude.

Exeunt all the Commoners.

FLAVIUS	They vanish tongue-tied in their guiltiness.
	Go you down that way towards the Capitol,
	This way will I. Disrobe the images
	If you do find them deck'd with ceremonies.
MARULLUS	May we do so?
	You know it is the feast of Lupercal.
FLAVIUS	It is no matter, let no images
	Be hung with Caesar's trophies. I'll about
	And drive away the vulgar from the streets.
	These growing feathers pluck'd from Caesar's wing
	Will make him fly an ordinary pitch,
	Who else would soar above the view of man
	And keep us all in servile fearfulness. *Exeunt.*

Enter Caesar, Antony for the course, Calpurnia, Portia, Decius, Cicero, Brutus, Cassius, Casca, a Soothsayer; after them Marullus and Flavius, and a crowd following.

CAESAR	Set on, and leave no ceremony out.
ANTONY	When Caesar says, "Do this," it is perform'd.
SOOTHSAYER	Caesar.
CAESAR	Ha? Who calls?
CASCA	Bid every noise be still. Caesar speaks.
CAESAR	I hear a tongue shriller than all the music
	Cry "Caesar." Speak, Caesar is turn'd to hear.
SOOTHSAYER	Beware the ides of March.
CAESAR	What man is that?
BRUTUS	A soothsayer bids you beware the ides of March.
CAESAR	He is a dreamer, let us leave him. Pass.

Sennet. Exeunt all but Brutus and Cassius.

CASSIUS	Will you go see the order of the course?
BRUTUS	I am not gamesome. I do lack some part
	Of that quick spirit that is in Antony.
	Let me not hinder, Cassius, your desires.
CASSIUS	Brutus, I do observe you now of late.
	I have not from your eyes that gentleness
	And show of love as I was wont to have.
BRUTUS	Do not construe any further my neglect,
	Than that poor Brutus, with himself at war,
	Forgets the shows of love to other men.
CASSIUS	Then, Brutus, I have much mistook your passion.
	Flourish and shout.
BRUTUS	What means this shouting?
	I do fear the people choose Caesar for their King.
CASSIUS	Ay, do you fear it?
	Then must I think you would not have it so.
BRUTUS	I would not, Cassius, yet I love him well.

164

CASSIUS	I cannot tell what you and other men
	Think of this life, but for my single self
	I had as lief not be as live to be
	In awe of such a thing as I myself.
	I was born free as Caesar, yet this man
	Is now become a god, and Cassius is
	A wretched creature and must bend his body
	If Caesar carelessly but nod on him.
	Shout. Flourish.
BRUTUS	I do believe that these applauses are
	For some new honors that are heap'd on Caesar.
CASSIUS	Why, man, he doth bestride the narrow world
	Like a Colossus, and we petty men
	Walk under his huge legs and peep about
	To find ourselves dishonorable graves.
	The fault, dear Brutus, is not in our stars,
	But in ourselves, that we are underlings.
	Brutus and Caesar: what should be in that "Caesar"?
	Why should that name be sounded more than yours?

BRUTUS	How I have thought of this and of these times,
	I shall recount hereafter. For this present,
	Then, my noble friend, chew upon this:
	Brutus had rather be a villager
	Than to repute himself a son of Rome
	Under these hard conditions, as this time
	Is like to lay upon us.
CASSIUS	I am glad
	That my weak words have struck but thus much show
	Of fire from Brutus.
	Enter Caesar and his train.
BRUTUS	The games are done and Caesar is returning.
	The angry spot doth glow on Caesar's brow,
	And all the rest look like a chidden train.
CASSIUS	Casca will tell us what the matter is.
CAESAR	Antonio.
ANTONY	Caesar.
CAESAR	Let me have men about me that are fat,
	Sleek-headed men, and such as sleep a-nights.
	Yond Cassius has a lean and hungry look,
	He thinks too much: such men are dangerous.
ANTONY	Fear him not, Caesar, he's not dangerous.
CAESAR	Would he were fatter, but I fear him not.
	I rather tell thee what is to be fear'd
	Than what I fear, for always I am Caesar.
	Exeunt Caesar and his train.
BRUTUS	Casca, tell us what hath chanc'd today
	That Caesar looks so sad.
CASCA	Why, there was a crown offer'd him, and being offer'd him, he put it by with the back of his hand, thus — but, to my thinking, he would fain have had it — and then the people fell a-shouting.
BRUTUS	What was the second noise for?
CASCA	Why, for that too.
CASSIUS	They shouted thrice, what was the last cry for?
CASCA	Why, for that too.
BRUTUS	Was the crown offer'd him thrice?
CASCA	Ay, marry was 't, and he put it by thrice, every time gentler than other; and at every putting-by mine honest neighbors shouted.
CASSIUS	Who offer'd him the crown?
CASCA	Why, Antony.
BRUTUS	And after that he came thus sad, away?
CASCA	Ay.
CASSIUS	Did Cicero say anything?
CASCA	Ay, he spoke Greek.
CASSIUS	To what effect?

CASCA	Those that understood him smil'd at one another and shook their heads; but for mine own part, it was Greek to me. I could tell you more news too: Marullus and Flavius, for pulling scarfs off Caesar's images, are put to silence.
CASSIUS	Will you dine with me tomorrow?
CASCA	Ay, if I be alive and your mind hold, and your dinner worth the eating.
CASSIUS	Good, I will expect you.
CASCA	Do so. Farewell, both. *Exit.*
BRUTUS	What a blunt fellow is this grown to be. He was quick mettle when we went to school.
CASSIUS	So is he now in execution Of any bold or noble enterprise.
BRUTUS	Tomorrow, if you please to speak with me, I will come home to you; or, if you will, Come home to me.
CASSIUS	Till then, think of the world. *Exit Brutus.* I will this night in at his windows throw Writings, all tending to the great opinion That Rome holds of his name, wherein obscurely Caesar's ambition shall be glanced at. And after this, let Caesar seat him sure, For we will shake him, or worse days endure. *Exit.*

The next three scenes are concerned with the happenings of one long stormy night. On this threatening night there is little sleep for those destined to play principal roles in the events to take place on the coming day, the fateful ides of March. The ominous tone, first sounded by the Soothsayer in Scene 1, booms loudly now through every speech: in the street, in Brutus's garden, at Caesar's house.

Cassius meets Casca in the dark, rain-drenched streets. He leads him to believe that the heavens have been thrown into confusion by Caesar's arrogant ambition, and enlists him in the conspiracy.

Brutus struggles all night against his love for Caesar, but finally convinces himself Caesar must die, when he reads the note thrown into his window by Cassius — the note that he thinks comes from the citizens of Rome.

Despite the warnings of nature and the pleadings of his wife, Caesar is persuaded to go to the Senate by Decius, who sways him with a three-pronged argument: he calms Caesar's super-

*stitious fears, he promises him a crown, and finally he threatens
that people will laugh at him if he stays at home.*

When morning comes, the conspiracy is complete.

Scene 2

Thunder and lightning. Enter Casca and Cassius.

CASSIUS   Who's there?

CASCA   A Roman.

CASSIUS   Casca, by your voice.

CASCA   Your ear is good. Cassius, what night is this?
Who ever knew the heavens menace so?

CASSIUS   Those that have known the earth so full of faults.

CASCA   Are not you mov'd, when all the sway of earth
Shakes like a thing unfirm? A common slave
Held up his left hand, which did flame and burn
Like twenty torches join'd; and yet his hand,
Not sensible of fire, remain'd unscorch'd.
And yesterday the bird of night did sit,
Even at noonday, upon the market place,
Hooting and shrieking. When these prodigies
Do so conjointly meet, let not men say,
"These are their reasons, they are natural."
For I believe they are portentous things.

CASSIUS   If you would consider the true cause
Why all these things change from their ordinance
To monstrous quality, why, you shall find
That heaven hath infus'd them with these spirits
To make them instruments of fear and warning
Unto some monstrous state.
Now could I, Casca, name to thee a man
Most like this dreadful night,
A man no mightier than thyself, or me,
In personal action, yet prodigious grown,
And fearful as these strange eruptions are.

CASCA   'Tis Caesar that you mean, is it not, Cassius?

CASSIUS   Let it be who it is.

CASCA   They say the senators
                         Mean to establish Caesar as a King.
CASSIUS   I know where I will wear this dagger then,
                         Cassius from bondage will deliver Cassius.
CASCA   So every bondman in his own hand bears
                         The power to cancel his captivity.
CASSIUS   Those that with haste will make a mighty fire,
                         Begin it with weak straws. What trash is Rome,
                         What rubbish, and what offal, when it serves
                         For the base matter to illuminate
                         So vile a thing as Caesar. But, O Grief,
                         Where hast thou led me? I perhaps speak this
                         Before a willing bondman.
CASCA   You speak to Casca,
                         That is no fleering telltale. Hold, my hand.
                         Be factious for redress of all these griefs,
                         And I will set this foot of mine as far
                         As who goes furthest.
CASSIUS   There's a bargain made.
                         Now know you, Casca, I have mov'd already
                         Some certain of the noblest-minded Romans
                         To undergo, with me, an enterprise
                         Of honorable-dangerous consequence.
                         Come, Casca, you and I will yet, ere day,
                         See Brutus at his house; three parts of him
                         Is ours already, and the man entire
                         Upon the next encounter yields him ours.
CASCA   O he sits high in all the people's hearts,
                         And that which would appear offense in us,
                         His countenance, like richest alchemy,
                         Will change to virtue and to worthiness.
CASSIUS   Him, and his worth, and our great need of him,
                         You have right well conceited. Let us go.   *Exeunt.*

Scene 3

Enter Brutus in his orchard.
BRUTUS   What, Lucius, ho!
                         Enter Lucius.

LUCIUS	Call'd you, my lord?
BRUTUS	Get me a taper in my study, Lucius.
	When it is lighted, come and call me here.
LUCIUS	I will, my lord. *Exit.*
BRUTUS	It must be by his death, and for my part
	I know no personal cause to spurn at him,
	But for the general. He would be crown'd.
	How that might change his nature, there's the question.
	Fashion it thus: that what he is, augmented,
	Would run to these and these extremities,
	And therefore think him as a serpent's egg
	Which hatch'd, would, as his kind, grow mischievous,
	And kill him in the shell.
	Enter Lucius.
LUCIUS	The taper burneth in your closet, sir.
	Searching the window for a flint, I found
	This paper, thus seal'd up, and I am sure
	It did not lie there when I went to bed. *Gives him the letter.*
BRUTUS	Get you to bed again, it is not day. *Exit Lucius.*
	The exhalations whizzing in the air
	Give so much light that I may read by them.
	Opens the letter and reads.
	"Brutus, thou sleep'st; awake, and see thyself.
	Shall Rome, etc. Speak, strike, redress!" —
	"Brutus, thou sleep'st; awake."
	"Shall Rome, etc." Thus must I piece it out:
	Shall Rome stand under one man's awe? What, Rome?
	My ancestors did from the streets of Rome
	The Tarquin drive, when he was call'd a King.
	"Speak, strike, redress!" Am I entreated
	To speak, and strike? O Rome, I make thee promise,
	If the redress will follow, thou receivest
	Thy full petition at the hand of Brutus.
	Knocking within. Enter Lucius.
LUCIUS	Sir, 'tis your brother Cassius at the door,
	Who doth desire to see you.
BRUTUS	Is he alone?
LUCIUS	No, sir, there are moe with him.
BRUTUS	Do you know them?
LUCIUS	No, sir; their hats are pluck'd about their ears,
	And half their faces buried in their cloaks.
BRUTUS	Let 'em enter. *Exit Lucius.*
	O Conspiracy,
	Sham'st thou to show thy dang'rous brow by night,
	When evils are most free? O then, by day

171

Where wilt thou find a cavern dark enough
To mask thy monstrous visage? Seek none, Conspiracy,
Hide it in smiles and affability.
Enter the Conspirators, Cassius, Casca, Decius, Cinna, Metellus,
and Trebonius.

CASSIUS   Good morrow, Brutus; do we trouble you?

BRUTUS   I have been up this hour, awake all night.
Know I these men that come along with you?

CASSIUS   Yes, every man of them; and no man here
But honors you; and every one doth wish
You had but that opinion of yourself
Which every noble Roman bears of you.
This is Trebonius.

BRUTUS   He is welcome hither.

CASSIUS   This, Decius Brutus.

BRUTUS   He is welcome too.

CASSIUS   This, Casca; this, Cinna; and this, Metellus Cimber.

BRUTUS   They are all welcome.

CASSIUS   Shall I entreat a word?
Cassius and Brutus whisper.

DECIUS   Here lies the east; doth not the day break here?

CASCA   No.

CINNA   O pardon, sir, it doth, and yon gray lines
That fret the clouds are messengers of day.

CASCA   Here, as I point my sword, the sun arises.
Some two months hence, up higher toward the north
He presents his fire, and the high east
Stands, as the Capitol, directly here.

BRUTUS   Give me your hands all over, one by one.

CASSIUS   And let us swear our resolution.

BRUTUS   No, not an oath. What need we any spur
But our own cause? And what other oath
Than honesty to honesty engag'd,
That this shall be, or we will fall for it?

CASSIUS   But what of Cicero? Shall we sound him?

METELLUS   O let us have him, for his silver hairs
Will purchase us a good opinion
And buy men's voices to commend our deeds.

BRUTUS   O name him not; let us not break with him,
For he will never follow anything
That other men begin.

CASSIUS   Then leave him out.

DECIUS   Shall no man else be touch'd, but only Caesar?

CASSIUS   Decius, well urg'd. I think it is not meet

	Mark Antony, so well belov'd of Caesar,
	Should outlive Caesar.
BRUTUS	Our course will seem too bloody,
	To cut the head off and then hack the limbs;
	For Antony is but a limb of Caesar.
	Let's be sacrificers, but not butchers, Caius.
	And for Mark Antony, think not of him,
	For he can do no more than Caesar's arm
	When Caesar's head is off.
CASSIUS	Yet I fear him.

Clock strikes.

BRUTUS	Peace, count the clock.
CASSIUS	The clock hath stricken three.
TREBONIUS	'Tis time to part.
CASSIUS	But it is doubtful yet
	Whether Caesar will come forth today or no.
DECIUS	Never fear that. If he be so resolv'd,
	I can o'ersway him. Let me work,
	And I will bring him to the Capitol.
CASSIUS	Nay, we will all of us be there to fetch him.
BRUTUS	By the eighth hour, is that the uttermost?
CINNA	Be that the uttermost, and fail not then.
CASSIUS	The morning comes upon 's; we'll leave you, Brutus.
BRUTUS	Good gentlemen, look fresh and merrily;
	Let not our looks put on our purposes.
	And so good morrow to you every one. *Exeunt all but Brutus.*
	Boy! Lucius! Fast asleep? It is no matter.
	Thou hast no figures nor no fantasies
	Which busy care draws in the brains of men;
	Therefore thou sleep'st so sound.

Enter Portia.

PORTIA	Brutus, my lord.
BRUTUS	Portia, what mean you? Wherefore rise you now?
	It is not for your health thus to commit
	Your weak condition to the raw, cold morning.
PORTIA	Nor for yours neither. Dear my lord,
	Make me acquainted with your cause of grief.
BRUTUS	I am not well in health, and that is all.
PORTIA	Brutus is wise, and were he not in health,
	He would embrace the means to come by it.
BRUTUS	Why, so I do.
PORTIA	What, is Brutus sick,
	And will he steal out of his wholesome bed
	To dare the vile contagion of the night

To add unto his sickness? No, my Brutus,
You have some sick offense within your mind.
I grant I am a woman, but, withal,
A woman that Lord Brutus took to wife;
I grant I am a woman, but, withal,
A woman well reputed, Cato's daughter.
Think you I am no stronger than my sex,
Being so father'd and so husbanded?
Tell me your counsels, I will not disclose 'em.

BRUTUS   O ye gods!
Render me worthy of this noble wife.
By and by thy bosom shall partake
The secrets of my heart. Go in with me.   *Exeunt.*

174

Scene 4

Thunder and lightning. Enter Caesar in his nightgown.

CAESAR
Nor heaven nor earth have been at peace tonight:
Thrice hath Calpurnia in her sleep cried out,
"Help, ho! They murther Caesar!" Who's within?
Enter Calpurnia.

CALPURNIA
What mean you, Caesar? Think you to walk forth?
You shall not stir out of your house today.

CAESAR
Caesar shall forth.

CALPURNIA
       There is one within
Recounts most horrid sights seen by the watch.
Fierce fiery warriors fought upon the clouds,
Horses did neigh, and dying men did groan,
And ghosts did shriek and squeal about the streets.
O Caesar, these things are beyond all use.

CAESAR
Yet Caesar shall go forth, for these predictions
Are to the world in general as to Caesar.

CALPURNIA
When beggars die there are no comets seen;
The heavens themselves blaze forth the death of princes.

CAESAR
Cowards die many times before their deaths,
The valiant never taste of death but once.
It seems to me most strange that men should fear,
Seeing that death, a necessary end,
Will come when it will come.
Enter a Servant.   What say the augurers?

SERVANT
They would not have you stir forth today.
Plucking the entrails of an offering forth,
They could not find a heart within the beast.

CAESAR
The gods do this in shame of cowardice:
Caesar should be a beast without a heart
If he should stay at home today for fear.
No, Caesar shall not.

CALPURNIA
       Alas, my lord,
Your wisdom is consum'd in confidence.
We'll send Mark Antony to the Senate House,

	And he shall say you are not well today.
	Let me, upon my knee, prevail in this.
CAESAR	For thy humor, I will stay at home.
	Here's Decius Brutus, he shall tell them so.
	Enter Decius.
DECIUS	Caesar, all hail! Good morrow, worthy Caesar,
	I come to fetch you to the Senate House.
CAESAR	Bear my greeting to the senators
	And tell them that I will not come today.
	Cannot, is false, and that I dare not, falser.
	I will not come today, tell them so, Decius.
CALPURNIA	Say he is sick.
CAESAR	Shall Caesar send a lie?
	Decius, go tell them Caesar will not come.
	That is enough to satisfy the Senate,
	But for your private satisfaction,
	Because I love you, I will let you know.
	Calpurnia here, my wife, stays me at home.
	She dreamt tonight she saw my statue,
	Which, like a fountain with a hundred spouts,
	Did run pure blood, and many lusty Romans
	Came smiling and did bathe their hands in it.
	And these she applies for warnings; and on her knee
	Hath begg'd that I will stay at home today.
DECIUS	This dream is all amiss interpreted;
	It was a vision fair and fortunate:
	Your statue spouting blood in many pipes,
	In which so many smiling Romans bath'd,
	Signifies that from you great Rome shall suck
	Reviving blood. The Senate have concluded
	To give this day a crown to mighty Caesar.
	If you shall send them word you will not come,
	Their minds may change. Besides, it were a mock
	Apt to be render'd, for some one to say,
	"Break up the Senate till another time,
	When Caesar's wife shall meet with better dreams."
CAESAR	How foolish do your fears seem now, Calpurnia!
	I am ashamed I did yield to them.
	And look where Publius is come to fetch me.
	Enter Publius, Brutus, Metellus, Casca, Trebonius, Cinna, and Cassius.
PUBLIUS	Good morrow, Caesar.
CAESAR	Welcome, Publius.
	What, Brutus, are you stirr'd so early too?
	What is 't o'clock?

BRUTUS	Caesar, 'tis strucken eight.

Enter Antony.

CAESAR	See, Antony, that revels long a-nights,
	Is notwithstanding up. Good morrow, Antony.
	Good friends, go in and taste some wine with me,
	And we, like friends, will straightway go together.
BRUTUS	*Aside.* That every like is not the same, O Caesar,
	The heart of Brutus yearns to think upon. *Exeunt.*

Scene 5

The ides of March are come.

The fates, through Artemidorus, make one last effort to save Caesar from his doom, but Caesar, whose wisdom is truly consumed in confidence, pushes the warning aside.

The conspirators work their way close to Caesar, and then strike. At that the people flee, to gather later in mobs, threatening Brutus and Cassius. But Brutus by his reasonable arguments persuades them that Caesar, not Brutus, was the real traitor to Rome. Then, thinking that they are thoroughly convinced, he further proves his love for Caesar by allowing Mark Antony to say a few words in Caesar's praise. That is Brutus's tragic mistake. For Antony, in a masterful speech, referring always to Brutus as an "honorable" man, so inflames the fickle mob that Brutus and Cassius must flee for their lives.

With the arrival of Caesar's nephew Octavius, the Roman people will again be embroiled in civil war.

Enter Artemidorus, reading.

ARTEMIDORUS	"Caesar, beware of Brutus; take heed of Cassius, come not near Casca, have an eye to Cinna, trust not Trebonius, mark well Metellus Cimber, Decius Brutus loves thee not. There is but one mind in all these men, and it is bent against Caesar. If thou beest not immortal, look about you. Security gives way to conspiracy. The mighty gods defend thee. — Thy lover, Artemidorus."
	Here will I stand till Caesar pass along,

And as a suitor will I give him this.
If thou read this, O Caesar, thou mayest live;
If not, the Fates with traitors do contrive.
Enter Portia and Lucius.

PORTIA   I prithee, boy, run to the Senate House;
Stay not to answer me, but get thee gone.
Why dost thou stay?

LUCIUS   To know my errand, madam.

PORTIA   I would have had thee there, and here again.
O constancy, be strong upon my side;
I have a man's mind, but a woman's might.
Art thou here yet?

LUCIUS   Madam, what should I do?
Run to the Capitol, and nothing else?
And so return to you, and nothing else?

PORTIA   Yes, bring me word, boy, if thy lord look well,
For he went sickly forth. What noise is that?

LUCIUS   I hear none, madam.

PORTIA   Prithee, listen well:
I hear a bustling rumor, like a fray.

LUCIUS   Sooth, madam, I hear nothing.

PORTIA   O Brutus,
The heavens speed thee in thine enterprise.
Run, Lucius, and commend me to my lord.
And bring me word what he doth say to thee.
                   Exeunt Portia and Lucius.
Flourish. Enter Caesar, Brutus, Cassius, Casca, Decius, Metellus, Trebonius, Cinna, Antony, Lepidus, Publius, Soothsayer, and Senators.

CAESAR   The ides of March are come.

SOOTHSAYER   Ay, Caesar, but not gone.

ARTEMIDORUS   Hail, Caesar! Read this schedule.

DECIUS   Trebonius doth desire you to o'er-read,
At your best leisure, this his humble suit.

ARTEMIDORUS   O Caesar, read mine first, for mine's a suit
That touches Caesar nearer. Read it, great Caesar.

CAESAR   What touches us ourself shall be last serv'd.

ARTEMIDORUS   Delay not, Caesar, read it instantly.

CAESAR   What, is the fellow mad?

PUBLIUS   Sirrah, give place.

CASSIUS   *Aside.* Trebonius knows his time, for, look you, Brutus,
He draws Mark Antony out of the way.

CINNA   *Aside.* Casca, you are the first that rears your hand.

CAESAR   Are we all ready? What is now amiss
That Caesar and his Senate must redress?

METELLUS	Most high, most mighty, and most puissant Caesar,
	Metellus Cimber throws before thy seat
	An humble heart —
CAESAR	I must prevent thee, Cimber.
	Thy brother by decree is banished.
	If thou dost bend, and pray, and fawn for him,
	I spurn thee like a cur out of my way.
BRUTUS	I kiss thy hand, but not in flattery, Caesar;
	Desiring thee that Publius Cimber may
	Have an immediate freedom of repeal.
CAESAR	What, Brutus!
CASSIUS	Pardon, Caesar; Caesar, pardon.
CAESAR	I am constant as the northern star,
	Of whose true-fix'd and resting quality
	There is no fellow in the firmament.
	I was constant Cimber should be banish'd,
	And constant do remain to keep him so.
CINNA	O Caesar.
CAESAR	Hence! Wilt thou lift up Olympus?
CASCA	Speak, hands, for me.
	They stab Caesar.
CAESAR	Et tu, Brute? — Then fall, Caesar! *Dies.*
CINNA	Liberty! Freedom! Tyranny is dead!
	Run hence, proclaim, cry it about the streets.
BRUTUS	People and senators, be not affrighted.
	Fly not, stand still; ambition's debt is paid.
	Where's Publius?
CINNA	Here, quite confounded with this mutiny.
BRUTUS	There is no harm intended to your person,
	Nor to no Roman else; so tell them, Publius.
CASSIUS	And leave us, Publius, lest that the people,
	Rushing on us, should do your age some mischief.
BRUTUS	Do so; and let no man abide this deed
	But we the doers.
	Enter Trebonius.
CASSIUS	Where is Antony?
TREBONIUS	Fled to his house amaz'd.
BRUTUS	Stoop, Romans, stoop,
	And let us bathe our hands in Caesar's blood.
	Then walk we forth, even to the market place,
	And all cry, "Peace, freedom, and liberty."
CASSIUS	Stoop then, and wash. How many ages hence
	Shall this our lofty scene be acted over,

	In states unborn and accents yet unknown!
BRUTUS	How many times shall Caesar bleed in sport,
	That now on Pompey's basis lies along,
	No worthier than the dust?
CASSIUS	So oft as that shall be,
	So often shall the knot of us be call'd
	The men that gave their country liberty.
	Enter Antony.
BRUTUS	But here comes Antony. Welcome, Mark Antony.
ANTONY	O mighty Caesar! Dost thou lie so low?
	I know not, gentlemen, what you intend,
	Who else must be let blood, who else is rank.
	If I myself, there is no hour so fit
	As Caesar's death's hour, nor no instrument
	Of half that worth as those your swords, made rich
	With the most noble blood of all this world.
BRUTUS	O Antony! Beg not your death of us.
	Though now we must appear bloody and cruel,
	Our hearts you see not, they are pitiful;
	And pity to the general wrong of Rome
	Hath done this deed on Caesar. For your part,
	To you our swords have leaden points, Mark Antony.
CASSIUS	Your voice shall be as strong as any man's
	In the disposing of new dignities.
BRUTUS	Only be patient, till we have appeas'd
	The multitude, beside themselves with fear,
	And then we will deliver you the cause
	Why I, that did love Caesar when I struck him,
	Have thus proceeded.
CASSIUS	Will you be prick'd in number of our friends,
	Or shall we on, and not depend on you?
ANTONY	Friends am I with you all, and love you all,
	Upon this hope, that you shall give me reasons
	Why and wherein Caesar was dangerous.
BRUTUS	Our reasons are so full of good regard
	That were you, Antony, the son of Caesar,
	You should be satisfied.
ANTONY	That's all I seek,
	And am moreover suitor that I may
	In the pulpit, as becomes a friend,
	Speak in the order of his funeral.
BRUTUS	You shall, Mark Antony.
CASSIUS	Brutus, do not consent
	That Antony speak in his funeral.
BRUTUS	I will myself into the pulpit first

	And show the reason of our Caesar's death,
	And that we are contented Caesar shall
	Have all true rites and lawful ceremonies.
	It shall advantage more than do us wrong.
CASSIUS	I know not what may fall, I like it not.
BRUTUS	*To Antony.* You shall not in your funeral speech blame us,
	But speak all good you can devise of Caesar,
	And say you do 't by our permission;
	And you shall speak after my speech is ended.
ANTONY	I do desire no more.
BRUTUS	Prepare the body then. *Exeunt all but Antony.*
ANTONY	O pardon me, thou bleeding piece of earth,
	That I am meek and gentle with these butchers.
	Over thy wounds now do I prophesy,
	Domestic fury and fierce civil strife
	Shall cumber all the parts of Italy;
	And Caesar's spirit, ranging for revenge,
	With Ate by his side come hot from hell,
	Shall in these confines with a monarch's voice
	Cry "Havoc!" and let slip the dogs of war,
	That this foul deed shall smell above the earth
	With carrion men, groaning for burial.
	Enter Brutus and Cassius, with the Plebeians.
PLEBEIANS	We will be satisfied; let us be satisfied.
BRUTUS	Then follow me, and give me audience, friends,
	And public reasons shall be rendered
	Of Caesar's death.
FIRST PLEB.	The noble Brutus is ascended: silence!
BRUTUS	Be patient till the last.

Romans, countrymen, and lovers, hear me for my cause, and be silent, that you may hear. Believe me for mine honor, and have respect to mine honor, that you may believe. Censure me in your wisdom, and awake your senses, that you may the better judge. If there be any in this assembly, any dear friends of Caesar's, to him I say that Brutus' love to Caesar was no less than his. If then that friend demand why Brutus rose against Caesar, this is my answer: Not that I lov'd Caesar less, but that I lov'd Rome more. Had you rather Caesar were living, and die all slaves; than that Caesar were dead, to live all free men? As Caesar lov'd me, I weep for him; as he was fortunate, I rejoice at it; as he was valiant, I honor him; but, as he was ambitious, I slew him. There is tears, for his love; joy, for his fortune; honor, for his valor; and death, for his ambition. Who is here so base, that would be a bondman? If any, speak, for him have I offended. Who is here so rude, that would not be

	a Roman? If any, speak, for him have I offended. Who is here so vile, that will not love his country? If any, speak, for him have I offended. I pause for a reply.
PLEBEIANS	None, Brutus, none.
BRUTUS	Here lies his body, mourn'd by Mark Antony, who, though he had no hand in his death, shall receive the benefit of his dying, a place in the commonwealth, as which of you shall not? With this I depart: that, as I slew my best lover for the good of Rome, I have the same dagger for myself, when it shall please my country to need my death.
PLEBEIANS	Live, Brutus! Live! Live!
FIRST PLEB.	Let him be Caesar.
SECOND PLEB.	Caesar's better parts shall be crown'd in Brutus.
BRUTUS	My countrymen.
THIRD PLEB.	Peace! Silence! Brutus speaks.
BRUTUS	Good countrymen, let me depart alone,
	And, for my sake, stay here with Antony.
	Do grace to Caesar's corpse, and grace his speech
	Tending to Caesar's glories, which Mark Antony,
	By our permission, is allow'd to make. *Exit.*
FIRST PLEB.	Stay, ho, and let us hear Mark Antony.
ANTONY	For Brutus' sake, I am beholding to you.
FOURTH PLEB.	'Twere best he speak no harm of Brutus here!
FIRST PLEB.	This Caesar was a tyrant.
THIRD PLEB.	Nay, that's certain.
	We are bless'd that Rome is rid of him.
ANTONY	You gentle Romans —
PLEBEIANS	Peace, ho, let us hear him.
ANTONY	Friends, Romans, countrymen, lend me your ears.
	I come to bury Caesar, not to praise him.
	The evil that men do lives after them,
	The good is oft interred with their bones;
	So let it be with Caesar. The noble Brutus
	Hath told you Caesar was ambitious;
	If it were so, it was a grievous fault,
	And grievously hath Caesar answer'd it.
	Here, under leave of Brutus and the rest —
	For Brutus is an honorable man,
	So are they all, all honorable men —
	Come I to speak in Caesar's funeral.
	He was my friend, faithful and just to me;
	But Brutus says he was ambitious,
	And Brutus is an honorable man.
	He hath brought many captives home to Rome,
	Whose ransoms did the general coffers fill.

Did this in Caesar seem ambitious?
When that the poor have cried, Caesar hath wept;
Ambition should be made of sterner stuff,
Yet Brutus says he was ambitious,
And Brutus is an honorable man.
You all did see that on the Lupercal
I thrice presented him a kingly crown,
Which he did thrice refuse. Was this ambition?
Yet Brutus says he was ambitious,
And, sure, he is an honorable man.
You all did love him once, not without cause,
What cause withholds you then to mourn for him?
O judgment! Thou art fled to brutish beasts,
And men have lost their reason. Bear with me,
My heart is in the coffin there with Caesar,
And I must pause, till it come back to me.

FIRST PLEB.	Methinks there is much reason in his sayings.
SECOND PLEB.	If thou consider rightly of the matter,
	Caesar has had great wrong.
FOURTH PLEB.	He'd not take the crown,
	Therefore 'tis certain he was not ambitious.
ANTONY	Here's a parchment with the seal of Caesar;
	I found it in his closet, 'tis his will.
	Let but the commons hear this testament
	And they would go and kiss dead Caesar's wounds,
	And dip their napkins in his sacred blood,
	Yea, beg a hair of him for memory,
	And, dying, mention it within their wills,
	Bequeathing it as a rich legacy
	Unto their issue.
PLEBEIANS	The will, the will; we will hear Caesar's will.
ANTONY	Have patience, gentle friends, I must not read it.
	It is not meet you know how Caesar lov'd you;
	You are not wood, you are not stones, but men,
	And being men, hearing the will of Caesar,
	It will inflame you, it will make you mad.
	'Tis good you know not that you are his heirs,
	For if you should, O what would come of it?
FOURTH PLEB.	Read the will, we'll hear it, Antony.
ANTONY	I have o'ershot myself to tell you of it.
	I fear I wrong the honorable men
	Whose daggers have stabb'd Caesar.
SECOND PLEB.	They were villains!
ANTONY	Let me show you him that made the will.
	If you have tears, prepare to shed them now.
	You all do know this mantle; I remember
	The first time ever Caesar put it on.
	Look, in this place ran Cassius' dagger through;
	See what a rent the envious Casca made;
	Through this, the well-beloved Brutus stabb'd,
	And as he pluck'd his cursed steel away,
	Mark how the blood of Caesar follow'd it,
	As rushing out of doors to be resolv'd
	If Brutus so unkindly knock'd, or no;
	For Brutus, as you know, was Caesar's angel.
	Judge, O you gods, how dearly Caesar lov'd him.
	This was the most unkindest cut of all.
	For when the noble Caesar saw him stab,
	Ingratitude, more strong than traitors' arms,
	Quite vanquish'd him; then burst his mighty heart,
	And in his mantle muffling up his face,

	At the base of Pompey's statue great Caesar fell.
FIRST PLEB.	O piteous spectacle!
THIRD PLEB.	O noble Caesar!
FOURTH PLEB.	O traitors, villains!
SECOND PLEB.	Revenge! About! Seek! Burn! Fire!
	Kill! Slay! Let not a traitor live!
ANTONY	Yet hear me, countrymen; yet hear me speak.
	You have forgot the will I told you of.
PLEBEIANS	Most true, the will, let's stay and hear the will.
ANTONY	Here is the will, and under Caesar's seal.
	To every Roman citizen he gives,
	To every several man, seventy-five drachmas.
SECOND PLEB.	Most noble Caesar!
THIRD PLEB.	We'll revenge his death.
ANTONY	Moreover, he hath left you all his walks,
	His private arbors, and new-planted orchards,
	To walk abroad and recreate yourselves.
	Here was a Caesar! When comes such another?
FIRST PLEB.	Never, never! Come, away, away!
	We'll burn his body in the holy place,
	And with the brands fire the traitors' houses.
	Take up the body.
SECOND PLEB.	Go, fetch fire. *Exeunt Plebeians, with Caesar's body.*
ANTONY	Now, let it work: Mischief, thou art afoot,
	Take thou what course thou wilt.
	Enter a Servant. How now, fellow?
SERVANT	Sir, Octavius is already come to Rome.
ANTONY	Where is he?
SERVANT	He and Lepidus are at Caesar's house.
ANTONY	And thither will I straight to visit him.
	He comes upon a wish. Fortune is merry,
	And in this mood will give us anything.
SERVANT	I heard him say Brutus and Cassius
	Are rid like madmen through the gates of Rome.
ANTONY	Belike they had some notice of the people,
	How I had mov'd them. Bring me to Octavius. *Exeunt.*
	Enter Cinna the poet, and after him the Plebeians.
CINNA	I dreamt tonight that I did feast with Caesar,
	And things unluckily charge my fantasy.
FIRST PLEB.	What is your name?
SECOND PLEB.	Whither are you going?
THIRD PLEB.	Where do you dwell?
FOURTH PLEB.	Are you a married man, or a bachelor?
SECOND PLEB.	Answer every man directly.
FIRST PLEB.	Ay, and briefly.

186

FOURTH PLEB.	Ay, and truly, you were best.
CINNA	To answer every man directly and briefly, wisely and truly: wisely I say, I am a bachelor.
SECOND PLEB.	That's as much as to say, they are fools that marry. Proceed directly.
CINNA	Directly, I am going to Caesar's funeral.
FIRST PLEB.	As a friend or an enemy?
CINNA	As a friend.
FOURTH PLEB.	For your dwelling, briefly.
CINNA	Briefly, I dwell by the Capitol.
THIRD PLEB.	Your name, sir, truly.
CINNA	Truly, my name is Cinna.
SECOND PLEB.	Tear him to pieces, he's a conspirator.
CINNA	I am Cinna the poet, I am Cinna the poet! I am not Cinna the conspirator.
FOURTH PLEB.	It is no matter, his name's Cinna. *Exit Cinna.*
THIRD PLEB.	Tear him, tear him; come, brands, ho! Firebrands!

Exeunt all the Plebeians.

Scene 6

Enter Antony, Octavius, and Lepidus.

ANTONY	These many then shall die; their names are prick'd.
OCTAVIUS	Your brother too must die; consent you, Lepidus?
LEPIDUS	I do consent.
OCTAVIUS	Prick him down, Antony.
LEPIDUS	Upon condition Publius shall not live, Who is your sister's son, Mark Antony.
ANTONY	He shall not live; look, with a spot I damn him. But, Lepidus, go you to Caesar's house, Fetch the will hither.
LEPIDUS	What, shall I find you here?
OCTAVIUS	Or here or at the Capitol. *Exit Lepidus.*
ANTONY	This is a slight unmeritable man, Meet to be sent on errands; is it fit, The threefold world divided, he should stand One of the three to share it?
OCTAVIUS	So you thought him.
ANTONY	Octavius, I have seen more days than you, And though we lay these honors on this man, He shall but bear them as the ass bears gold, Either led or driven, as we point the way;

187

And having brought our treasure where we will,
Then take we down his load, and turn him off,
Like to the empty ass, to shake his ears,
And graze in commons.

OCTAVIUS   You may do your will,
But he's a tried and valiant soldier.

ANTONY   So is my horse, Octavius. And now,
Listen great things. Brutus and Cassius
Are levying powers; we must straight make head;
Therefore let our alliance be combin'd,
Our best friends made, our means stretch'd.

OCTAVIUS   Let us do so, for we are at the stake,
And bayed about with many enemies.   *Exeunt.*

ACT II
Scene 1

*Brutus and Cassius fled separately to Thrace, raising troops as
they went. Now they join forces. After an exchange of bitter,
angry words, Brutus and Cassius pledge their love for each
other over a bowl of wine. Then with two of their officers they
hold a conference in Brutus's tent and plan their strategy
against Antony and Octavius. Night has fallen by the time the
conference is over. Brutus tries to get some rest, but he cannot
sleep. In the stillness of the middle of the night, he thinks the
ghost of Caesar appears to him. In his frenzy he awakens the
whole camp and they set off immediately to meet Antony and
Octavius at Philippi.*

Drum. Enter Brutus, Lucilius, and the Army.

BRUTUS   Stand ho!

LUCILIUS   Give the word ho, and stand!

BRUTUS   What now, Lucilius, is Cassius near?

LUCILIUS   He is at hand.

BRUTUS   A word, Lucilius;
How he receiv'd you, let me be resolv'd.

LUCILIUS   With courtesy and with respect enough,
But not with such familiar instances
As he hath used of old.

BRUTUS	Thou hast describ'd
	A hot friend, cooling. Comes his army on?
LUCILIUS	The greater part, the horse in general,
	Are come with Cassius.
BRUTUS	*Low march within.* Hark! He is arriv'd.
	Enter Cassius and his Army.
CASSIUS	Stand ho!
	Most noble brother, you have done me wrong.
BRUTUS	Judge me, you gods! Wrong I mine enemies?
	And if not so, how should I wrong a brother?
CASSIUS	Brutus, this sober form of yours hides wrongs,
	And when you do them —
BRUTUS	Cassius, be content.
	Before the eyes of both our armies here
	Let us not wrangle. Bid them move away,
	And I will give you audience.
CASSIUS	Pindarus,
	Bid our commanders lead their charges off
	A little from this ground.
BRUTUS	Lucilius, do you the like, and let no man
	Come to our tent till we have done our conference.
	Let Lucius and Titinius guard our door.
	Exeunt all but Brutus and Cassius.
	Let me tell you, Cassius, that you
	Are much condemn'd to have an itching palm,
	To sell and mart your offices for gold
	To undeservers.
CASSIUS	I an itching palm!
BRUTUS	Remember March, the ides of March remember:
	Did not great Julius bleed for justice' sake?
	What villain touch'd his body, that did stab,
	And not for justice? What, shall one of us,
	That struck the foremost man of all this world,
	Contaminate our fingers with base bribes?
	I had rather be a dog and bay the moon,
	Than such a Roman.
CASSIUS	Brutus, bait not me,
	I'll not endure it. I am a soldier, I,
	Older in practice, abler than yourself
	To make conditions.
BRUTUS	Go to; you are not, Cassius.
CASSIUS	I am.
BRUTUS	I say you are not.
CASSIUS	Urge me no more, I shall forget myself.
BRUTUS	Must I give way and room to your rash choler?

189

Shall I be frighted when a madman stares?

CASSIUS Must I endure all this?

BRUTUS   From this day forth,
I'll use you for my mirth, yea, for my laughter,
When you are waspish.

CASSIUS   Is it come to this?
Do not presume too much upon my love;
I may do that I shall be sorry for.

BRUTUS You have done that you should be sorry for.
There is no terror, Cassius, in your threats.
I sent to you for gold, which you denied me,
For I can raise no money by vile means;
By heaven, I had rather coin my heart,
And drop my blood for drachmas, than to wring
From the hard hands of peasants their vile trash
By indirection. I did send
To you for gold to pay my legions,
Which you denied me.

CASSIUS   I denied you not.

BRUTUS You did.

CASSIUS   I did not. He was but a fool
That brought my answer back. Brutus hath riv'd my heart:
You love me not.

BRUTUS   I do not like your faults.

CASSIUS Come, Antony, and young Octavius, come,
Revenge yourselves alone on Cassius,
Hated by one he loves; his faults observ'd,
Set in a notebook, learn'd, and conn'd by rote,
To cast into my teeth. There is my dagger.
Strike as thou didst at Caesar, for I know
When thou didst hate him worst, thou lov'dst him better
Than ever thou lov'dst Cassius.

BRUTUS   Sheathe your dagger.
O Cassius, you are yoked with a lamb
That carries anger as the flint bears fire,
Who, much enforced, shows a hasty spark,
And straight is cold again.

CASSIUS   Hath Cassius liv'd
To be but mirth and laughter to his Brutus,
When grief and blood ill-temper'd vexeth him?

BRUTUS When I spoke that I was ill-temper'd too.

CASSIUS Do you confess so much? Give me your hand.

BRUTUS And my heart too.

CASSIUS O Brutus!

BRUTUS What's the matter?

190

CASSIUS	I did not think you could have been so angry.
BRUTUS	O Cassius, I am sick of many griefs.
	Portia is dead.
CASSIUS	How scap'd I killing when I cross'd you so?
	O insupportable and touching loss!
	Upon what sickness?
BRUTUS	Impatient of my absence,
	And grief that young Octavius with Mark Antony
	Have made themselves so strong, she fell distract,
	And, her attendants absent, swallow'd fire.
CASSIUS	And died so?
BRUTUS	Even so.
CASSIUS	O ye immortal gods!
BRUTUS	Speak no more of her. Lucius, a bowl of wine.
	Enter Lucius, with wine and taper.
	In this I bury all unkindness, Cassius. *Drinks.*
CASSIUS	My heart is thirsty for that noble pledge.
	I cannot drink too much of Brutus' love. *Drinks.*

Exit Lucius.

BRUTUS	Come in, Titinius.
	Enter Titinius and Messala.
	Welcome, good Messala.
	Young Octavius and Mark Antony
	Come down upon us with a mighty power,
	Bending their expedition toward Philippi.
MESSALA	Myself have letters of the selfsame tenor.
BRUTUS	With what addition?
MESSALA	That by proscription and bills of outlawry,
	Octavius, Antony, and Lepidus,
	Have put to death an hundred senators.
BRUTUS	Therein our letters do not well agree;
	Mine speak of seventy senators that died
	By their proscriptions, Cicero being one.
CASSIUS	Cicero one?
MESSALA	Cicero is dead.
BRUTUS	Well, to our work alive. What do you think
	Of marching to Philippi presently?
CASSIUS	I do not think it good.
BRUTUS	Your reason?
CASSIUS	This it is:
	'Tis better that the enemy seek us;
	So shall he waste his means, weary his soldiers,
	Doing himself offense, whilst we, lying still,
	Are full of rest, defense, and nimbleness.
BRUTUS	Good reasons must, of force, give place to better.

	Our legions are brimful, our cause is ripe;

Our legions are brimful, our cause is ripe;
The enemy increaseth every day,
We, at the height, are ready to decline.
There is a tide in the affairs of men,
Which, taken at the flood, leads on to fortune;
Omitted, all the voyage of their life
Is bound in shallows and in miseries.
On such a full sea are we now afloat,
And we must take the current when it serves,
Or lose our ventures.

CASSIUS   Then, with your will, go on: we'll along
Ourselves, and meet them at Philippi.

BRUTUS   The deep of night is crept upon our talk,
And nature must obey necessity.

CASSIUS   Early tomorrow will we rise, and hence.

BRUTUS   Good night, and good repose.

CASSIUS   O my dear brother,
Never come such division 'tween our souls;
Let it not, Brutus.

BRUTUS   Everything is well.

TITINIUS
MESSALA   Good night, Lord Brutus.

BRUTUS   Farewell, every one.   *Exeunt Cassius, Titinius, and Messala.*
Enter Lucius.

BRUTUS   Lucius, boy, where is thy instrument?

LUCIUS   Here, sir.

BRUTUS   What, thou speak'st drowsily?
Poor knave, I blame thee not, thou art o'erwatch'd.
Canst thou hold up thy heavy eyes awhile,
And touch thy instrument a strain or two?

LUCIUS   Ay, my lord, an 't please you.

BRUTUS   It does, my boy.
I trouble thee too much, but thou art willing.

LUCIUS   It is my duty, sir.

BRUTUS   I will not hold thee long. If I do live,
I will be good to thee.
Music, and a song; Lucius sleeps.
This is a sleepy tune. Gentle knave, good night;
I will not do thee so much wrong to wake thee.
If thou dost nod, thou break'st thy instrument;
I'll take it from thee, and, good boy, good night.
Enter the Ghost of Caesar.
How ill this taper burns. Ha! Who comes here?
I think it is the weakness of mine eyes
That shapes this monstrous apparition.

	It comes upon me. Art thou any thing?	
	Art thou some god, some angel, or some devil,	
	That mak'st my blood cold and my hair to stare?	
	Speak to me what thou art.	
GHOST	Thy evil spirit, Brutus.	
BRUTUS	Why com'st thou?	
GHOST	To tell thee thou shalt see me at Philippi.	
BRUTUS	Well, then I shall see thee again?	
GHOST	Ay, at Philippi.	
BRUTUS	Why, I will see thee at Philippi then.	*The Ghost vanishes.*
	Now I have taken heart, thou vanishest.	
	Ill spirit, I would hold more talk with thee.	
	Boy, Lucius! Lucius, sir, awake!	

LUCIUS	My lord!
BRUTUS	Go, and commend me to my brother Cassius.
	Bid him set on his powers betimes before,
	And we will follow.
LUCIUS	It shall be done, my lord. *Exeunt.*

Scene 2

At Philippi the armies meet. On one side of the field are the
armies of Octavius and Antony; on the other side are those of
Brutus and Cassius — with armor shining and banners waving.
The generals hold a parley in which they challenge each other
to fight, and the battle is joined. Now,

> "Let us
> On your imaginary forces work.
> Suppose within the girdle of these walls
> Are now confined two mighty [armies].
> Piece out our imperfections with your thoughts;
> Into a thousand parts divide one man;
> And make imaginary puissance;
> Think, when we talk of horses, that you see them
> Printing their proud hoofs i' th' receiving earth.
> For 'tis your thoughts that now must deck our [stage]."

Drum. Enter Octavius, Antony, and their Army.

OCTAVIUS	Now, Antony, our hopes are answered.
	You said the enemy would not come down.
	It proves not so; their battles are at hand,
	They mean to warn us at Philippi here.
ANTONY	Tut! They come down with fearful bravery
	To fasten in our thoughts that they have courage;
	But 'tis not so.
	Enter a Messenger.
MESSENGER	Prepare you, generals,
	The enemy comes on in gallant show.
	Drum. Enter Brutus, Cassius, and their Army.
BRUTUS	They stand, and would have parley.
OCTAVIUS	Mark Antony, shall we give sign of battle?
ANTONY	No, Caesar, we will answer on their charge.
BRUTUS	*To Antony and Octavius.*
	Words before blows: is it so, countrymen?

194

OCTAVIUS	Not that we love words better, as you do.
BRUTUS	Good words are better than bad strokes, Octavius.
ANTONY	In your bad strokes, Brutus, you give good words;
	Witness the hole you made in Caesar's heart,
	Crying "Long live! Hail, Caesar!"
OCTAVIUS	Look, I draw a sword against conspirators;
	When think you that the sword goes up again?
	Never, till Caesar's three and thirty wounds
	Be well aveng'd; or till another Caesar
	Have added slaughter to the sword of traitors.
BRUTUS	Caesar, thou canst not die by traitors' hands,
	Unless thou bring'st them with thee.
OCTAVIUS	Come, Antony, away!
	Defiance, traitors, hurl we in your teeth.
	If you dare fight today, come to the field;
	If not, when you have stomachs.

CASSIUS Why now, blow wind, swell billow, and swim bark!
The storm is up, and all is on the hazard!
If we do lose this battle, then is this
The very last time we shall speak together.

BRUTUS This same day
Must end the work the ides of March begun.
And whether we shall meet again, I know not.
Therefore our everlasting farewell take:
Forever, and forever, farewell, Cassius.
If we do meet again, why, we shall smile;
If not, why then this parting was well made.

CASSIUS Forever, and forever, farewell, Brutus.
If we do meet again, we'll smile indeed;
If not, 'tis true, this parting was well made.

BRUTUS Why then, lead on. O, that a man might know
The end of this day's business, ere it come;
But it sufficeth that the day will end,
And then the end is known. Come, ho! Away!   *Exeunt.*

There can be only glimpses of the battle as it progresses, although the sounds of battle are all around — trumpet calls, drum rolls, shouts of soldiers, clash of swords. On the little corner of the battlefield represented by the stage, small groups of soldiers charge by into battle, flee in terror, or pause to rest for a moment.

At first all goes well for Brutus: his soldiers seem to be defeating Octavius's army, and he presses his advantage. But Cassius's luck is not so good. Antony's army surrounds him, and his soldiers turn and run away.

Alarum. Enter Brutus and Messala.

BRUTUS Ride, ride, Messala, ride and give these bills
Unto the legions on the other side.
Let them set on at once, for I perceive
But cold demeanor in Octavius' wing,
And sudden push gives them the overthrow.   *Exeunt.*

Alarum. Enter Cassius and Titinius.

CASSIUS O look, Titinius, look, the villains fly.
This ensign here of mine was turning back;
I slew the coward, and did take it from him.

TITINIUS	O Cassius, Brutus gave the word too early,
	Who, having some advantage on Octavius,
	Took it too eagerly; his soldiers fell to spoil,
	Whilst we by Antony are all enclos'd.
	Enter Pindarus.
PINDARUS	Mark Antony is in your tents, my lord.
	Fly, therefore, noble Cassius, fly far off.
CASSIUS	This hill is far enough. Look, look, Titinius;
	Mount thou my horse, and hide thy spurs in him,
	Till he have brought thee up to yonder troops
	And here again, that I may rest assur'd
	Whether yond troops are friend or enemy.
TITINIUS	I will be here again, even with a thought. *Exit.*
CASSIUS	Go, Pindarus, get higher on that hill,
	And tell me what thou not'st about the field.
	This is my birthday; time is come round,
	And where I did begin, there shall I end.
PINDARUS	*Above.* O my lord!
CASSIUS	What news?
PINDARUS	Titinius is enclosed round about
	With horsemen that make to him on the spur.
	O, he's ta'en. *A shout.*
	And hark, they shout for joy.
CASSIUS	Come down, behold no more.
	Come hither, sirrah.
	In Parthia did I take thee prisoner,
	And then I swore thee, saving of thy life,
	That whatsoever I did bid thee do,
	Thou shouldst attempt it. Come now, keep thine oath;
	Now be a freeman, and with this good sword,
	That ran through Caesar's bowels, search this bosom.
	Stand not to answer — Caesar, thou art reveng'd,
	Even with the sword that kill'd thee. *Dies.*
PINDARUS	So, I am free, yet would not so have been,
	Durst I have done my will. O Cassius,
	Far from this country Pindarus shall run,
	Where never Roman shall take note of him. *Exit.*
	Enter Titinius and Messala.
MESSALA	It is but change, Titinius; for Octavius
	Is overthrown by noble Brutus' power,
	As Cassius' legions are by Antony.
TITINIUS	These tidings will well comfort Cassius.
MESSALA	Where did you leave him?
TITINIUS	All disconsolate,

	With Pindarus his bondman, on this hill.
MESSALA	Is not that he that lies upon the ground?
	Is not that he?
TITINIUS	No, this was he, Messala.

But Cassius is no more. Our day is gone;
Mistrust of my success hath done this deed.

MESSALA O hateful error, Melancholy's child.

TITINIUS What, Pindarus? Where art thou, Pindarus?

MESSALA Seek him, Titinius, whilst I go to meet
The noble Brutus, thrusting this report
Into his ears.

TITINIUS Hie, therefore, Messala. *Exit Messala.*
Why didst thou send me forth, brave Cassius?
Did I not meet thy friends, and did not they
Put on my brows this wreath of victory,
And bid me give it thee? Didst thou not hear their shouts?
Alas, thou hast misconstrued everything.
But hold thee, take this garland on thy brow;
Thy Brutus bid me give it thee, and I
Will do his bidding. This is a Roman's part:
Come, Cassius' sword, and find Titinius' heart. *Dies.*
Alarum. Enter Brutus, Messala, Young Cato, Strato, and Lucilius.

BRUTUS Where, where, Messala, doth his body lie?

MESSALA Lo, yonder, and Titinius mourning it.

CATO Titinius is slain.

BRUTUS O Julius Caesar, thou art mighty yet!
Thy spirit walks abroad and turns our swords
In our own proper entrails.
Low Alarums.

CATO Brave Titinius!
Look whe'r he have not crown'd dead Cassius.

BRUTUS Are yet two Romans living such as these?
The last of all the Romans, fare thee well.
It is impossible that ever Rome
Should breed thy fellow. Let us to the field.
'Tis three o'clock, and, Romans, yet ere night
We shall try fortune in a second fight! *Exeunt.*

From here on it becomes increasingly clear that Antony and Octavius are destined to be victorious. One after another, Brutus's friends die or are captured. When Lucilius is captured, he makes a desperate attempt to give Brutus a chance to escape; he pretends that he is Brutus and tries to bribe Antony's soldiers to kill him. But his effort is in vain. Brutus is doomed to die.

Alarum. Enter Brutus, Messala, Young Cato, and Lucilius.

BRUTUS   Yet, countrymen, O yet hold up your heads!

CATO   What bastard doth not? Who will go with me?

I am the son of Marcus Cato, ho!

A foe to tyrants, and my country's friend.

BRUTUS   And I am Brutus, Marcus Brutus, I;

Brutus, my country's friend; know me for Brutus!   *Exit.*

Enter Soldiers, and fight. Young Cato falls.

LUCILIUS   O young and noble Cato, art thou down?

Why now thou diest as bravely as Titinius.

FIRST SOLDIER   Yield, or thou diest.

LUCILIUS   Only I yield to die.

There is so much that thou wilt kill me straight.

Kill Brutus, and be honor'd in his death.

FIRST SOLDIER   We must not. A noble prisoner.

SECOND SOLDIER   Tell Antony, Brutus is ta'en.

Enter Antony.

FIRST SOLDIER   Here comes the general.

Brutus is ta'en, Brutus is ta'en, my lord.

ANTONY   Where is he?

LUCILIUS   Safe, Antony; Brutus is safe enough.

I dare assure thee that no enemy

Shall ever take alive the noble Brutus.

ANTONY   This is not Brutus, friend, but, I assure you,

A prize no less in worth. I had rather have

Such men my friends than enemies. Go on,

And see whe'r Brutus be alive or dead.   *Exeunt.*

Enter Brutus, Dardanius, Clitus, Strato, and Volumnius.

BRUTUS   Come, poor remains of friends, rest on this rock.

CLITUS   Statilius show'd the torchlight, but, my lord,

He came not back. He is or ta'en or slain.

BRUTUS   "Slaying" is the word;

It is a deed in fashion. Hark thee, Clitus. *Whispers.*

CLITUS   What I, my lord? No, not for all the world.

BRUTUS   Peace, then, no words. Hark thee, Dardanius. *Whispers.*

DARDANIUS   Shall I do such a deed?

CLITUS   What ill request did Brutus make to thee?

DARDANIUS   To kill him, Clitus. Look, he meditates.

CLITUS   Now is that noble vessel full of grief.

BRUTUS   Come hither, good Volumnius, list a word.

VOLUMNIUS   What says my lord?

BRUTUS   Why, this, Volumnius:

	The ghost of Caesar hath appear'd to me
	Two several times by night; at Sardis once,
	And, this last night here in Philippi fields.
	I know my hour is come.
VOLUMNIUS	Not so, my lord.
BRUTUS	Nay, I am sure it is. Volumnius,
	Thou know'st that we two went to school together;
	Even for that our love of old, I prithee,
	Hold thou my sword hilts whilst I run on it.
VOLUMNIUS	That's not an office for a friend, my lord.
	Alarums.
CLITUS	Fly, fly, my lord, there is no tarrying here.
BRUTUS	Farewell to you, and you, and you, Volumnius.
	My heart doth joy that yet, in all my life
	I found no man but he was true to me.
	So fare you well at once. *Exeunt Dardanius and Volumnius.*
	Alarum. Cry within, "Fly, fly, fly."
CLITUS	Fly, my lord, fly!
BRUTUS	Hence, I will follow. *Exit Clitus.*
	I prithee, Strato, stay thou by thy lord.
	Thy life hath had some smatch of honor in it;
	Hold then my sword, and turn away thy face,
	While I do run upon it. Wilt thou, Strato?
STRATO	Give me your hand first. Fare you well, my lord.
BRUTUS	Farewell, good Strato — Caesar, now be still,
	I kill'd not thee with half so good a will. *Dies.*
	Alarum. Retreat. Enter Octavius, Antony, Messala, Lucilius, and the Army.
OCTAVIUS	What man is that?
MESSALA	My master's man. Strato, where is thy master?
STRATO	Free from the bondage you are in, Messala.
LUCILIUS	So Brutus should be found.
ANTONY	This was the noblest Roman of them all;
	All the conspirators save only he
	Did that they did in envy of great Caesar;
	He, only in a general honest thought
	And common good to all, made one of them.
	His life was gentle, and the elements
	So mix'd in him that Nature might stand up
	And say to all the world, "This was a man!" *Exeunt.*

Production Notes

SHAKESPEARE's plays were written to be acted. Exciting though it may be to read them, it is only when they are performed that they come fully to life. Fortunately, a production need not be lavish to be good. Shakespeare's plays can be produced without elaborate sets, without fancy costumes — without even a stage — but they cannot be produced without hard work. With some effort, however, these short versions can be performed by children as young as ten years — performed well, with understanding and pleasure — and they are worth all the effort they cost.

Each of the plays in this volume will run for about an hour in performance. Six weeks of rehearsals should result in a fairly finished performance (one-hour rehearsals, except for the last few).

So far as the actual staging is concerned, there is only one imperative: keep the play moving. One scene must follow another with no more pause than the end of a paragraph brings in reading. The surest way to guarantee a bored and restless audience is to make them wait through long, dreary intervals while elaborate scenery is shifted or costumes are changed. I recommend that the plays be performed without any intermission at all — which is the way Shakespeare probably performed them himself.

SCENERY

In planning a set, remember that the greatest resource the designer has is the imagination of the audience, and keep the scenery simple. It is far better to suggest than to try to depict. As a matter of fact, it is frequently necessary that no definite locale be represented. Within the space of a few lines Shakespeare sometimes jumps from what is clearly one place (if you stop long enough to think about it) to what is clearly another, with no break in the action. Take as an example *Julius Caesar*, Act I, Scene 5. The early part of this scene obviously occurs in the street leading to the Capitol, whereas later it is just as obviously inside the Capitol building. However, if the audience is caught up in what is taking place, it matters not a whit where it is taking place. *Julius Caesar* was produced successfully by a fifth grade without any scenery at all. It was acted semi-arena style on the floor of the auditorium, with the audience on three sides of the playing area. The set consisted of a two-step platform and a small box. Nothing more.

COSTUMES

These, too, must be simple. Again, suggest rather than depict, remembering always that, no matter what he may call them, Shakespeare's characters are sixteenth-century Englishmen blood and bone, the kind he knew in London and Stratford. Furthermore, in Shakespeare's time little effort was made to costume a play in keeping with the time and place in which it was laid. Therefore, strict historical accuracy is not necessary for them. Costumes evocative of Elizabethan times are called for generally, although earlier and simpler styles will do for characters of lowly estate.

A long, loose gown with its fullness falling from the neckline is a good basic costume for the girls; for the boys, a short tunic (doublet) over tights. If your costume committee includes mothers who, though enthusiastic, are inept with needle and thread, you might find sleeveless tunics over blouses or shirts a happy solution. Modify these basic costumes to suit the different characters and the various plays. Handsome costumes can be made of inexpensive lining satins and taffetas, or something as simple as an old pillowcase with openings for arms and head will frequently do very well. The problem of footwear can be solved in several ways. For example, neutral-colored socks worn over the tights, with a cuff at midcalf, make acceptable substitutes for boots. The best solution, however, is inexpensive acrobatic dance rehearsal sandals, which look almost medieval.

All men except those of the lowest classes should wear some linen, a simple white collar at least; a useful model is the Chandos portrait of Shakespeare. Characters with higher social status could wear ruffs; they might also wear short puffed breeches with their doublets. Add a hat or two, and perhaps a cape, and the play is costumed.

Above all, avoid complicated costume changes during a play. If a change is absolutely necessary, add an accessory, or remove one. For example, in A Midsummer Night's Dream the four lovers who have wandered all night in the woods appear almost immediately afterward at their own wedding celebration. Even in this situation it is enough to add bright silk sleeveless jerkins over the boys' doublet and hose, and wreaths of flowers for the girls' hair.

LIGHTING

If your theater has good lighting equipment, use it by all means. Shakespeare would have used it if he had had it. But he didn't, so lighting effects are not necessary in his plays; he always has his characters tell the audience anything they need to know about the time and the weather. In addition, he occasionally gives a visual cue as an aid to the imagination — a candle or a torch brought on by a servant. But don't be carried away. A long list of properties and an inexperienced backstage crew do not go well together.

MUSIC

Here is an essential ingredient in Shakespeare's plays. Besides many songs and dances, he calls for a variety of offstage effects to make the audience aware of events taking place elsewhere — music for an offstage banquet in *Macbeth,* hunting horns, trumpet calls, drum marches — as well as music to set the stage for scenes of pomp and pageantry like, for example, Julius Caesar's Triumph. And he makes free use of it as accompaniment to anything supernatural: fairies, spirits, and apparitions.

Many composers have been inspired to provide musical settings for the plays, but the music that seems to me best suited to them is music from the same time, the same world, that produced the plays themselves. The music given here is drawn from popular songs and instrumental pieces of the Elizabethan period, such as were commonly used in plays of the time. There are melody lines for the songs with chord indications suitable for guitar or piano. Incidental pieces are arranged for piano. Thus, with nothing more than a piano, the musical part of the production can be complete. Add a guitar to accompany songs, add trumpets, horns, and drums where indicated, and you have a varied and appropriate musical background. Piano settings for the songs, and orchestrations of the instrumental pieces, by Norman Cazden, are available from Composers Facsimile Edition, 170 West 74th Street, New York City.

SPEAKING

The last and most important consideration — so important it seems foolish even to mention it — is that the plays must be well spoken, with attention to, and delight in, the meanings, the sounds, and the rhythms.

Explore with your cast the many puns, from the outrageous ones of *The Comedy of Errors* to Lady Macbeth's sardonic "If he do bleed I'll *gild* the faces of the grooms withal, for it must seem their *guilt.*"

Point out the poetic devices Shakespeare uses, in particular, the alliteration: "wild waters," "hempen homespuns," "fierce fiery warriors." Young people enjoy the sounds as they hear them and the feel of the sounds as they pronounce them: *p*'s that pop and *t*'s that tickle their tongues, *f*'s and *v*'s that shiver against their teeth, and *m*'s that fill their heads with humming. This awareness of the consonants pays the further dividend of careful pronunciation — which in turn makes the lines easier for the audience to hear.

Enjoy with them the various rhythms, prose for some characters and situations, jingles for others. Call their attention especially to Shakespeare's versatility in the use of iambic pentameter, the heartbeat of his poetry; notice his development from the regular and (for Shakespeare) monotonous poetry of *The Comedy of Errors,* where the sense is measured out in five-foot lines, to the wonderfully expressive broken rhythms of *Macbeth* and the subtle, singing rhythms of *The Tempest.* In the later plays the meter is there, but so masterfully handled that the resulting language is as easy and natural as breathing.

Note further how the meter frequently affects pronunciation, for example, words ending in *-tion* and *-ed: -tion* is sometimes two syllables (pronounced *-shi-on* instead of *-shun*); *-ed* is a separate syllable (*fol-low-ed*) unless the word is written as a contraction (*fol-low'd*) — with the single exception of the word *used,* which is confusing when written *us'd.* With listening for the rhythm comes slower speaking, and with slower speaking, more audibility. Fortunately, it does not take long for the strangeness of such pronunciations to wear off.

Finally, no one can fail to take great delight in the wonderful richness of expression. These two so different references to night, for example:

Four happy days will steep themselves
   in night,
Four nights will quickly dream away the
   time.

Light thickens, and the crow
Makes wings to th' rooky wood.
Good things of day begin to droop and
   drowse,
Whiles night's black agents to their preys
   do rouse.

On and on it could go. Select for emphasis whatever you yourself enjoy most.

There are so many riches in Shakespeare that some can be overlooked — and should be, if the only reason for touching on them is that you think you ought to. In essence, you can increase your cast's pleasure (and, incidentally, slow their speaking) by making them aware of the delights in every word and phrase.

To sum up these general remarks: Keep the play moving, keep the production simple, and give loving care (but never reverence) to the speaking of the lines.

The Tempest

The Tempest provides an excellent opportunity for drama and music departments to work together. In this play the music is of major importance, because it is by means of music that Shakespeare creates and maintains the mood of unreality, of enchantment, that pervades the play: "The isle is full of noises, sounds and sweet airs." Ariel's songs are probably more important to the total effect than is the plot. Of the fifteen pages devoted here to music, six are specifically for *The Tempest.* One piece warrants special mention: the catch referred to in Act II, Scene 2. According to the script this catch is never sung. I suggest, however, that a very effective beginning for that scene would be for Trinculo, Stephano, and Caliban to enter singing the catch.

This play can be performed anywhere, on a stage, in a gymnasium or large classroom, or out of doors, because no set is necessary. The only requirement is a high place from which Prospero watches and controls the other characters in the play. The plan suggested here deliberately avoids representing anything. Up right of center there is simply a pile of boxes, to be sat on, climbed upon, and leaned against. You may think of them as stones and boulders if you wish. This is Prospero's high place. Caliban crawls out from behind it when he makes his first entrance, and Ferdinand stacks logs behind it, thus keeping his action on stage yet getting the logs out of the way for later scenes. The particular grouping illustrated here is made of two standard wooden foot-

The Setting

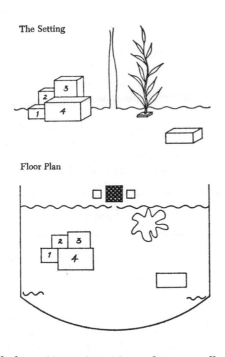

Floor Plan

Prospero will draw back the curtain to reveal Ferdinand and Miranda playing chess.

Except for the Prologue the whole play can be performed in this setting. One way to handle the Prologue would be to have Prospero stand on the highest box, listening to the voices, which come from offstage. Alternatively, the curtains might remain closed during the Prologue, with the voices coming from behind them. Or the scene can be played on the apron in semidarkness. In this case, one of the characters might carry a lantern to light their faces; everything else would be in shadow.

Most of the magic in the play is, of course, the music. There is one technical trick, however: the "quaint device" by which the banquet disappears. One way to get around the problem is to have each of the spirits bring in some item of food (roast goose, bowl of fruit, large bunches of grapes, etc.), which they set on the boxes up right (grapes could be hung on the tree). When Ariel appears to denounce the three villains, the other spirits reappear with him; when he claps his wings (or his hands), they disappear again, taking the food.

For this play costumes should look as rich as possible. With the exception of the seamen and Caliban, all the characters are of, or closely associated with, the nobility. On the other hand, they are travelers. Therefore, simple styles are appropriate: puffed breeches and short doublets made of handsome fabrics, with simple white collars instead of elaborate ruffs. Prospero must have a long cloak, the symbol of his magic art. A simple dress of thin soft material, preferably white, would be lovely for

lockers, 30″ × 18″ × 14″, and two smaller boxes, but any can be used, so long as they provide steps for Prospero to mount. For safety, the boxes should be securely nailed together. They should be painted a neutral color (gray, perhaps) and ideally the stage should be hung with neutral (gray) curtains. The one bit of color is the tree or plant, which is obviously make-believe. Besides being decorative this plant should be strong enough to serve as a hat tree on which Prospero and Ariel hang the "glistering apparel" for Stephano and Trinculo in Act II, Scene 4. The entrance to Prospero's cell is beside the tree, through a center opening in the curtains. Late in Act II

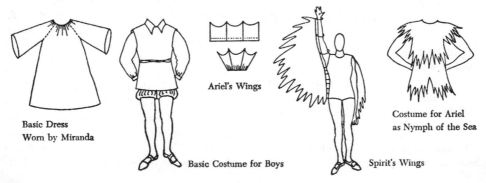

Basic Dress
Worn by Miranda

Basic Costume for Boys

Ariel's Wings

Spirit's Wings

Costume for Ariel
as Nymph of the Sea

Miranda. Seamen of this period wore full, baggy pants, gathered below the knee, and short jackets (or jerkins), with or without shirts. Model the Master of the ship after Captain John Smith or Sir Francis Drake.

Costumes for the spirits and Caliban can be as imaginative as one wishes to make them. The ones suggested here are quite effective, and fairly easy to make. The spirits wear leotards and tights, with a dusting of sequins or other glitter. Ariel has small wings attached to the back of his leotard close to the zipper; the wings are ruffles of stiff net, each made from a strip about 9″ × 24″, with one edge cut in three inverted scallops. The straight edge is gathered and sewed to the leotard. The ribs are pipe cleaners threaded through the holes in the net. As a nymph of the sea, Ariel puts on a short loose shift of china silk, cut in great jags around the bottom and sleeves; a long back opening with a single hook at the neck allows the wings to come through. A grotesque false face makes him a harpy. For the other spirits, cut jagged semicircles from thin china silk; attach the straight edge of a semicircle to the underarm and side seams of the leotard, from wrist to hip. Later, when the spirits are supposed to be dogs, they add false faces.

Caliban could be dressed in a tattered knee-length doublet, with a large square of rough burlap tied around his shoulders for a cloak (this is his gabardine, under which Trinculo hides). He would probably be barefooted, with a stooping, hunchbacked posture.

One word about pronunciation. It is obvious from the meter that Shakespeare accented the word Milan on the first syllable rather than the second. The place is of no significance in the play; Prospero might just as easily have been the Duke of Erewhon or of Oz. Therefore, preserve the poetry, which is important, and pronounce it Mi′lan.

Properties:
 wand for Prospero
 logs for Caliban and Ferdinand
 pipe and tabor for Ariel
 bottles for Stephano and Trinculo
 food for spirits
 glistering apparel
 swords
 clubs for Stephano and Trinculo
 lantern (optional)

A Midsummer Night's Dream

This play, Shakespeare says, is laid in mythological Athens. But can you imagine this Theseus threading his way through the Minoan labyrinth to find and slay the Minotaur? Of course not. This Theseus is a young lord of Queen Elizabeth's court who for the moment is acting a part in a court masque. This Hippolyta is an English gentlewoman, not a wild half-naked warrior Amazon. Bottom and friends would look ridiculous in Greek chitons with vine leaves in their hair; they are as English as Yorkshire pudding. Yet, add to these flesh-and-blood daytime characters the shadowy fairies, lovely and mischievous, dancing their fairy ring, then melting into the background before the mortals appear; add the four lovers in their nightlong, changing-partners chase through the moon-drenched woods; blend well with a touch of Puck — and you have a concoction that is not of this world, a dream surely.

And how, with paint and canvas, lumber and nails, does one fabricate a dream? I see nothing for it but to leave the whole problem to the audience. Give them an almost bare stage draped in pale gray curtains; before each scene tell them (by means of place signs) the direction in which to aim their imaginations; give them a bit of a push with appropriate music and one or two decorative props, and let them go.

A bower where Titania (and Bottom) can sleep unobserved is the only practical requirement, and even that could be dispensed with. However, the tracery of delicate Gothic arches up center would be both decorative as well as practical. Gold satin curtains hanging in the archway make a handsome background for the scenes in the Duke's palace. Open, they reveal a flower-decked nook for Titania; with a little stretch of the imagination the arches can even be thought of as the branches of trees. The arches pictured here are made of nar-

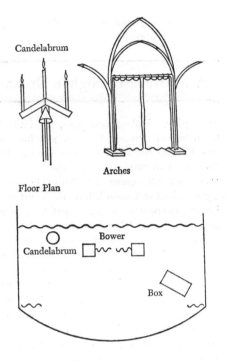

Candelabrum

Arches

Floor Plan

Candelabrum

Bower

Box

row (4-inch) strips of ⅛-inch Masonite, painted black, and wired to the uprights of a rigid frame made of iron pipe (about 6′ high × 5′ wide). The two halves of each of the arches are joined at the top with cloth tape. The half arches on each side are bowed by pieces of string or fine wire. On each upright of the archway place two spring clips (like broom holders) to hold branches of flowers during the forest scene. The only other items on stage are a candelabrum up right (for the scenes at the Duke's palace) and a box down left. Two

silk cushions grace the box during the palace scenes.

The mechanics of changing the scene from the palace to the woods and back again are very simple, and the curtains need never be closed. For the first scene a page enters with a sign saying "Athens, Palace of Theseus." Then, to a trumpet fanfare and preceded by an attendant carrying a banner, Theseus enters with Hippolyta on his arm. Between Scenes 1 and 2 a short musical interlude sets the mood for the woods scene; during it pages remove the cushions and candelabrum, in full view of the audience; fairies open the gold curtains and snap branches of flowers into their holders; and the page brings a sign, "A wood near Athens." During another musical interlude at the end of Scene 2 fairies remove the branches and close the curtains, and the pages bring back the candelabrum and cushions (four cushions this time, two for the box and two for the floor beside it). During the workmen's play members of the wedding party are grouped at stage left, Theseus and Hippolyta seated on the box, Hermia and Helena on the floor, the others standing behind them. The clowns have the right and center of the stage for their antics. After the fun is over and the court have left, a page snuffs out the candles or removes the candelabrum. And into the darkened palace slip the fairies.

With this kind of approach, the play can be performed anywhere, out of doors even in broad daylight, or in a bare gymnasium under glaring overhead lights. If it must be performed without effective stage lighting, let the colors the characters wear — and

Dress for Hermia   Dress for Helena

Jerkin over Doublet for

Dress for Hippolyta   Demetrius and Lysander   Costume for Theseus the poetry, of course — light the play.

The costumes fall into four categories: court, lovers, clowns, and fairies. Of these groups some appear always in darkness (the fairies), some always in light (Theseus and the court), some in both (the lovers and the clowns). Now, remembering that moonlight mutes colors, here is one way to attack the problem: dress members of the court in sunlight and torchlight colors (reds and golds) and the fairies in moonlight colors (gray-greens, dark green, and midnight-blue). Dark-colored velvet leotards are handsome for boy fairies, pale-colored chiffon shifts for girl fairies. Ruffles made of stiff net make lovely delicate wings. I think that Puck should be completely boyish: barefooted in tattered three-quarter-length blue jeans — made, however, of midnight-blue iridescent taffeta.

The other characters, who appear in both light and darkness, are more difficult. For the woods scene Demetrius and Lysander might wear dark purple and navy-blue doublets; for the first and last scenes add bright purple and royal-blue jerkins over their doublets. Dresses for Helena and Hermia could be pastels, color-keyed to their respective partners, one lavender, the other blue. In the last scene they add wreaths of gaily colored flowers for their hair.

Now for the clowns. Dull earth colors (browns, tans, grays, and black) suit both their characters and the nighttime scene, and are easily brightened up for their play before Theseus. Some of them add bright accessories to dark costumes: baggy gold pants and a huge white ruff make Quince a proper Prologue; a sandwich board with stones drawn on it turns Snout into Wall; a bright blue skirt and bonnet make Flute a colorful Thisby. Others remove dark accessories from lighter-colored basic costumes: Starveling might remove an apron to become Moonshine (with his various props); Bottom and Snug could remove dark jerkins; a rope tail and false face added to tawny-colored tights and doublet turn Snug into Lion; with a sword and an extravagantly plumed red hat, Bottom becomes gallant Pyramus.

The only thing remaining is an ass's head for Bottom. A comfortable one can be constructed from a false face, a jersey hood, and black yarn for a mane (a gauze false face, because gauze transmits sound better than other materials do).

"And I hope here is a play fitted."

Properties:
    candelabrum and snuffer (flames may be
        only gold and red paper)
    banner, carried by one of Theseus's at-
        tendants.
    four cushions
    branches of flowers
    scripts, for the workmen
    2 daggers, for Lysander and Demetrius
    wreath of flowers, for Titania to put on
        Bottom
    bows and spears, for attendants in the
        hunting scene
    scroll, for Philostrate
    scroll, for Quince as Prologue
    sword, for Bottom as Pyramus
    blood-stained mantle, for Flute as Thisby
    sandwich board, for Snout as Wall
    lion false face and rope tail, for Snug as
        Lion
    lantern, thornbush, and stuffed dog, for
        Starveling as Moonshine
    wreaths of flowers, for Hermia and Helena
    signs: Athens, The Palace of Theseus
        A Wood near Athens

The Comedy of Errors

Because *The Comedy of Errors* is first cousin to classical Latin comedy it calls for a setting in the classical tradition: a city street. Because it is cousin also to the popular *commedia dell'arte,* the costumes can be very gay, even a little zany.

The set suggested here uses three two-panel folding screens. One screen has 3-foot wide panels, the other two screens each have a 3-foot panel and a 2-foot panel. Six feet is a good height to make the frames, just tall enough not to be dwarfed by the actors, yet small enough to be handled easily. Made of 1″ × 3″ lumber and covered with thin wallboard (or heavy corrugated cardboard) they will be lightweight, rigid, and inexpensive. In addition to the

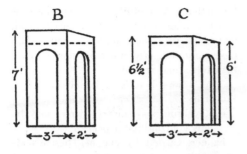

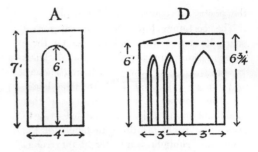

three screens, an archway is needed up center.

One other tradition is respected in planning the set for this play, that of the perspective stage setting of the Italian Renaissance. Some built-in perspective is achieved quite easily by extending the wallboard above the frames of the panels to different heights, and cutting the top edges of some of the panels at an angle (see the accompanying drawings; dotted lines indicate top edges of the frames).

The set is meant to suggest the arcaded galleries around an Italian piazza, or square. The two smaller screens (B and C) are at stage right, and have rounded Romanesque arches painted on them; scenes at Antipholus's house are played in front of them. The wider screen (D) is at stage left, with Gothic arches painted on it; the scene at the Priory has its focus here at stage left. None of the arches needs to be practical except the one up center. Characters enter around the sides of the screens and, if the situation warrants, the audience is willing to believe that they come from inside a house or church. It is not even necessary for screens to mask the entrances. The only reason for the upstage arch to be practical is that the Duke's entrances will be more dramatic if made through it rather than around it; this entrance up center should be reserved for the Duke and his attendants only. The entrance to Antipholus's house is between screens B and C. Entrances from the Priory are from up left, around the left side of screen D. Traffic along the street follows the curving Y-shaped arrow to and from up right (UR), up left (UL), and down left (DL).

In a play like this, where mistaken identity is all the fun, a device to avoid too much confusion on the part of the audience is helpful. Therefore, for most of their comings and goings on the streets of the city the Syracusan twins should use one street entrance (UL) and the Ephesian twins another (UR). The third street entrance (DL) leads to the goldsmith's shop; the Officer and anyone in his custody also use this entrance. At only one point will it be necessary to break these rules: when S. Dromio is sent by E. Antipholus to get money from Adriana. If Dromio goes on and off UL, he cannot avoid meeting S. Antipholus at the end of Scene 7. Therefore, for this one sequence only it would be better for Dromio to use UR.

Elizabethan styles are appropriate for the costumes, but you might like to take a cue from the clown ancestry of the Dromios and modify the costumes a little to enhance the gay mood of harliquinade: neck ruffs for everyone, for example, and bright circus colors — purple, turquoise, and royal blue; or purple, orange, and shocking pink.

Each pair of twins must, of course, be dressed exactly alike. The two Dromios might wear tights and short tunics with huge harlequin diamonds. The two Antipholuses might wear particolored tights and doublets with short jaunty capes hanging from their shoulders. (A little cutting and sewing makes two pairs of particolored tights out of two plain pairs of different colors.) Over basic dresses of thin crisp

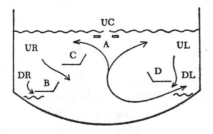

material, Adriana and Luciana could wear snugly-laced bodices dipping to a deep point in front, with ruffs at wrists as well as at the neck. The Duke might be dressed in extravagantly puffed breeches with a very short doublet, and Aemilia might wear a white habit (and ruff). A long black robe with cabalistic symbols on it, and a tall truncated-cone hat would be appropriate for Pinch (who is descended from *Dottore* of the *commedia dell'arte*, the quack doctor, the phony learned man).

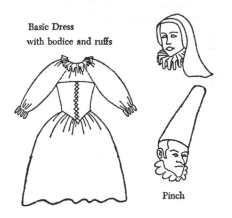

Basic Dress
with bodice and ruffs

Pinch

Properties:
    bag of money, for S. Antipholus to give to S. Dromio
    bag of money, for Luciana to give to S. Dromio
    rope, for E. Dromio
    gold chain, for Angelo to give to S. Antipholus
    swords, for S. Antipholus and Merchant
    halberds (long-handled battle axes), for the Duke's attendants

Macbeth

"Forbidding" is perhaps the word: the forbidding wilds of barbaric Scotland, the barren heath, the stark stone walls of castles, the pervading mood of evil, the powers of darkness. Forbidding, also, is the problem this play presents the set designer. The problem is to provide a setting that creates the proper mood and at the same time makes it possible for the scene to shift easily and quickly from the heath, to inside Macbeth's castle, to outside the castle, to inside again, to the witches' cavern, to England, to Birnam wood, back to Macbeth's castle — and sometimes to nowhere in particular.

I see no alternative to emphasizing the words of the play and letting the trappings take care of themselves, pretty much. The suggestions here are for an all-purpose set that is starkly simple, but, I hope, effective.

Gray, black, and red are, to me, the colors of *Macbeth*. Gray for the witches and the mists into which they melt, gray for the walls of castles, and the stones on the barren heath. Black for night and death and evil. And red for blood.

The setting proposed here again uses three folding screens. Again the wallboard covering extends beyond the edges of the six-foot frames; at its tallest point the center screen might be 8 feet high. The screens should be painted two shades of dark gray. This setting is designed primarily for a stage, although it can be adapted for a large classroom or gymnasium. With this setting the curtains need never be closed during the performance; they may be, if the director wishes, but it is not necessary. The screens serve equally well as background for scenes inside and outside the castle walls. Scenes that take place at some distance from the castle should in general be played on the apron of the stage in order to dissociate them from scenes clearly localized in or near the castle (although these latter will, and should, spill out onto the apron at times).

For the scene in the cavern with the witches (Act II, Scene 2) a special use of the center screen is suggested. The back of it is painted black, with gray stalactites. A triangular "floor" is nailed to the two panels at the bottom. On this floor sits a black cauldron over a bright red and orange fire (a cardboard cutout). One of the witches stands behind the screen, grasps the edges of the two panels, one in each hand, tilts the screen forward every so slightly, rotates it on its point — and there is the cavern. At the end of the scene she faces the fire, stretches out her bony arms, and is ready to turn the screen again. As she does so the two other witches vanish with her.

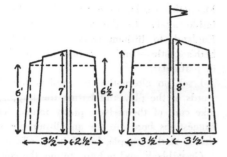

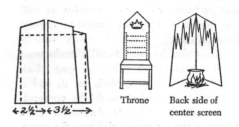

Throne   Back side of
center screen

At several points in the play properties need to be added to the set for various reasons, significant as well as practical.

(1) Before Act I, Scene 2, it is necessary to signal to the audience that the screens, which up to then may have seemed to be distant cliffs, must now become the enclosing walls of a castle. This may be accomplished by having servants cross the stage on various housekeeping errands; one servant brings a small stool (a black wooden box would be ideal) which he places down right of center. After that he stands at attention up center until Lady Macbeth enters, and then he leaves.

(2) Before Act II servants might bring on two ornate chairs — thrones to point up the fact that Macbeth is now King. (They will be useful later at the banquet.)

(3) To set the scene for the banquet, servants bring in a table, two benches, wine bowl, and tray of tankards during the musical prelude. At the end of the scene they must clear the table and remove the benches, table, and thrones before Scene 2 begins.

(4) In Act III, Scene 2, when Macbeth says "Hang out our banners on the outward walls," a soldier might place a flag on the angle of the center screen. Two small in-

conspicuous spring clips on the edge of the screen make it possible for him to do it quickly by snapping the flagpole into the clips.

The following four scenes (or parts of scenes) should be played almost entirely on the apron:

(1) Much of the first scene (on the heath) should be played on the apron, with the screens as distant background.

(2) Act III, Scene 1 (England). Malcolm and Macduff should enter at L, between the curtain and the proscenium arch; Ross comes to them up the steps to the stage (far DL). They all leave at L.

(3) In Act III, Scene 2, the exchange between Menteth, Cathness, Angus, and Lennox, who are now deserting Macbeth. Where they are is of no dramatic significance; but there is one place they clearly are not — the castle — although they may have left it only recently. Therefore, they might enter from DL, have their conversation on the apron, and exeunt at L to join Malcolm and the English.

(4) Later in Act III, Scene 2 (Birnam wood). Malcolm and his company should enter at L, where we saw them last, and exeunt down the steps, far DL, followed by the soldiers. They will soon come back up these same steps to storm the castle.

Which brings up another point. The approach to the stage by way of the steps is an effective one for any entrance when the characters come from a great distance. It was suggested above for Ross's arrival in England in Act III, Scene 1. It would be ideal in Act I, Scene 2, for Duncan's approach to Macbeth's castle — "This castle hath a pleasant seat." It could be used by Malcolm and Donalbain at the end of Act I when they depart for England and Ireland,

Floor Plan

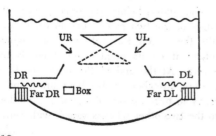

respectively. It should be used by the messenger in Act III, Scene 2, when he comes to report the approach of Birnam wood. And, certainly, for the storming of the castle: Malcolm would mount the steps to survey the castle and turn to give instructions to the soldiers below him. The fighting that follows would use the whole stage, apron, steps, and even perhaps the floor in front of the stage.

During the battle scene the stage direction "Alarums" (or "Alarum") appears three times. That is when the fighting takes place. At the first Alarum, Malcolm's soldiers race up the steps and are met by Macbeth's soldiers pouring out of the castle to drive them away, or be driven back themselves. As the stage clears for a moment Macbeth meets Young Siward. And so it goes.

Costumes for this play should be medieval rather than Elizabethan, since Macbeth lived in the eleventh century: knee-length tunics with sleeves but no collars, and knee stockings, some with tapes crisscrossed around them. This costume is adequate for most of the men most of the time. Over the tunic some would on occasion wear a coarse woolen cloak pinned on one shoulder with a large round brooch; a piece of colored burlap about 20 inches wide and 2 yards long makes an acceptable cloak. For battle scenes, add swords and, for a few characters, round shields. The doctor's tunic should be longer than the others', in keeping with the dignity of his profession.

Macbeth appears first in battle dress: black tunic and knee stockings, red cloak and shield. On his first entrance in Act I,

Scene 2, he appears without the shield; thereafter without the cloak. After he has become King he always wears a crown. On his first appearance as King (Act II, Scene 1) he wears over his tunic a regal red cape (a floor-length half-circle).

Lady Macbeth might wear a loose, long-sleeved, ankle-length black chemise (basic dress); over this, a shorter, more closely-fitted red gown with wide hanging sleeves; on her head, a thin black veil kept in place with a narrow band or circlet. As Queen she adds a red cape and crown. In the sleepwalking scene she wears only the black chemise. The gentlewoman wears similar garments.

Duncan wears a crown even on the battlefield. When he arrives for his visit with Macbeth, he wears a red cape, the symbol of kingship.

Siward and other English soldiers should be distinguishable from the Scots. They would not wear the rough woolen cloaks, nor the knee stockings. Instead they might wear tights and their tunics could be a little shorter.

The show of kings in the cavern scene can be managed with three actors circling around the center screen until there have been eight appearances. Dress them in crowns and the three red cloaks (Duncan's, Macbeth's, and Lady Macbeth's) that have already been established as the symbol of kingship.

Only the witches remain. They are crone-like, with long wispy gray hair, their garments hanging in long gray tatters that float in the wind as they move.

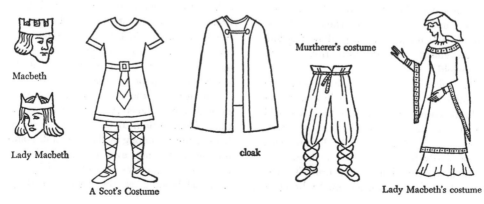

Macbeth

Lady Macbeth

A Scot's Costume

cloak

Murtherer's costume

Lady Macbeth's costume

Properties:
   box to serve as a stool
   letter, for Lady Macbeth
   wine bowl
   tray of tankards
   two daggers
   two thrones
   table
   two benches
   cauldron
   torches
   shields
   swords
   crowns

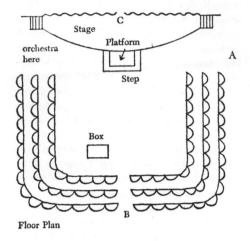

Floor Plan

Julius Caesar

The scope of *Julius Caesar* is so broad, so sweeping, that it is difficult to confine it to a conventional stage. It is the kind of play that cries out for an arena, or semi-arena, production, and that is what I recommend.

When it comes to costuming it, you face another very special problem. Like all Shakespeare's plays, it is permeated with the spirit of Elizabethan England, yet the story it tells is faithful to events that took place in Rome two thousand years ago. Add to that a theme that is timeless and both Roman and Elizabethan costumes seem somehow wrong. Which may explain why it has so often been performed in modern dress, a solution that only compounds the problem, it seems to me. Obviously, your actors have to wear something, but the costumes, like the setting, should go completely unnoticed, leaving only the dramatic conflict to absorb the attention of the audience. The costumes described here are, I hope, essentially timeless and unremarkable, with the further advantage that they allow freedom of movement, and go easily from city to battlefield.

The floor plan given here could be adapted for use in many auditoriums. An unlocalized playing space like this (it should be at least 20 feet square) can be street, forum, and battlefield, at will. Furthermore, it can easily become Brutus's orchard, or a room in Caesar's house. For Brutus's scene (Act I, Scene 3) Lucius might bring in (from entrance B) a tripod brazier, at which Brutus and the conspirators warm their hands; Brutus's house would then be thought of as being somewhere out entrance B. For Caesar's scene (Act I, Scene 4) a servant could bring in (from entrance A) a candelabrum and set it on the platform. Entrance A would, for that scene, be thought of as leading to other rooms in Caesar's house.

These two properties, the brazier and the candelabrum, serve two functions. They say that it is night, and they tip off the audience that the unlocalized playing space is being used differently. One other property would be appropriate in these nighttime scenes: when Cassius enters at the beginning of Scene 2, he might carry a torch.

The platform is useful in a variety of ways: Caesar will mount these steps when he goes up into the Capitol building; it is the pulpit from which Brutus and Antony deliver their funeral orations, with Caesar's body lying on the step where he fell; in Act II it will be, in turn, Brutus's tent, the hill from which Cassius watches the battle, and the rock on which Brutus rests at the end with his "poor remains of friends."

The apron of the stage, and the entrance through the curtains (C) add to the versatility of the setting. If the Soothsayer enters here at the beginning of the play and, pointing his finger out over the crowd below, cries out "Beware the ides of March," there is a heightening of the feeling of doom hanging over Caesar. It is useful for that in-between scene at the end of Act I where we see the newly formed triumvirate of Antony, Octavius, and Lepidus — already in the process of disintegration. It is very effective for the entrance of Caesar's ghost. It is excellent in the battle scenes. Brutus and Cassius stand here (with their standard-bearers at far left and right) to hurl insults and challenges across the field to Antony and Octavius near entrance B (with their armies trailing out behind them, down the aisle). When Octavius shouts back "Look, I draw a sword against conspirators!" he jumps up onto the box there. Later, during the battle, Octavius's soldiers attempt to storm the stage and are pushed back by Brutus's soldiers jumping off to drive them back out entrance B.

The basic costume suggested for this play is one designed for a fifth-grade production by the students and their art teacher. It is a short sleeveless and collarless tunic (literally, a pillowcase). Tights may be worn, but are not necessary. The color scheme uses all the warm colors, bright ones for patricians (yellow, orange, red), dull ones for plebeians (tans and browns). Draped over the tunic, the patricians wear bright-colored strips of cloth 6 inches wide and about 3 yards long. This strip of cloth distinguishes them from the plebeians (including servants) and suggests the toga worn in Caesar's time.

Only Caesar, the Soothsayer, and the two women need be dressed differently. Instead of a short tunic, Caesar might wear an ankle-length robe, preferably cream-colored or white. Over his robe and "toga" (of red) he should wear a purple cloak, and on his head a laurel wreath. The cloak can be simply a rectangular piece of cloth pinned around his shoulders. After Act I he substitutes a pale gray toga and cloak for the colored ones, and is ready to appear as his own ghost. Calpurnia and Portia might wear unbelted, sleeveless dresses with gracefully draped panels over the shoulder or around the neck. The Soothsayer would look properly ominous dressed in a long dark hooded cape, and leaning on a crooked cane.

Between Acts I and II all the actors must be turned into soldiers, quickly. A long drum march here would be excellent to set the scene and the mood for the war, and to allow the actors time to remove their togas and put on their armor. The armor suggested here consists of two triangles of silver or gold posterboard, joined with straps over the shoulders. Small capes (24-inch squares of cloth) might be fastened to the backs of the armor for the four generals — bright orange for Brutus and Cassius, blood-red for Antony and Octavius. Each soldier should have a short broadsword or dagger; there is no need to burden them with shields. In order to distinguish between the two opposing armies, the colors of their costumes now have new significance: the soldiers of Brutus and Cassius are the ones in light colors, tans, golds, and yellows, while those of Antony and Octavius are in dark colors, reds and browns.

With the addition of standards for the generals, the play is ready.

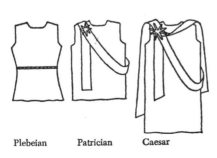

| Plebeian | Patrician | Caesar |

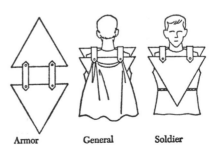

| Armor | General | Soldier |

Properties:
  cane, for the Soothsayer
  scepter with eagle, for Caesar (later for
    Octavius)
  torch, for Cassius
  brazier, for Brutus's house
  candelabrum, for Caesar's house

several papers or letters
small candle, for Brutus's tent
wine bowl, for Brutus's tent
lute, for Lucius
laurel wreath, for Titinius
standards for: Brutus, Cassius, and Antony
daggers or short swords

Sounds and Sweet Airs

Musical Numbers for the Plays

COME UNTO THESE YELLOW SANDS

Sung by Ariel and the spirits in *The Tempest*, Act I, Scene 1. [Set to the traditional tune "Nancie," as found in *The Fitzwilliam Virginal Book* (c. 1612).]

Ariel

Come un-to these yel-low sands, and then take hands: Curt-sied when you have, and kiss'd, the wild waves whist, Foot it feat-ly here and there, And sweet sprites the

Ariel

bur-then bear. Hark, hark! The watch-dogs bark, Hark, hark! The

Sprites [in two groups]

Bow wow! Bow wow!

watch-dogs bark, Hark, hark! Hark,

Bow wow, bow wow, wow wow! Bow wow!

hark! Hark, hark! I hear The strain of strut-ting Chan-ti-cleer

Bow wow! Bow wow!

Cry cock-a-did-dle-dow! Hark, hark! Hark, hark! Hark, hark! I

Bow wow! Bow wow, Bow wow!

Ariel

hear The strain of strut-ting Chan-ti-cleer Cry cock-a-did-dle-dow!

FULL FATHOM FIVE

Sung by Ariel, *Tempest*, Act I, Scene 1. [Composed by Robert Johnson, probably for the first performance of this play in 1611; known to have been used in 1613.]

Full fath-om five thy fa-ther lies; Of his bones are cor-al made; Those are pearls that were his eyes: Noth-ing of him that doth fade ——, But doth suf-fer a sea change In-to some-thing rich and strange. Sea nymphs hour-ly ring his knell. Hark, now I hear them! Hark ——, now I hear them! Ding-dong bell. Ding-dong, ding - dong bell ——————. Ding - dong, ding - dong bell ——————. Ding - dong, ding - dong bell ——————.

SOLEMN MUSIC

Played by Ariel, *Tempest*, Act I, Scene 2. The sound of a recorder group would be appropriate here. [Modeled on the song "Why Aske You" by Giles Farnaby in *The Fitzwilliam Virginal Book*.]

While You Here Do Snoring Lie

Sung by Ariel, *Tempest*, Act I, Scene 2. [Virtually the same melody as Solemn Music.]

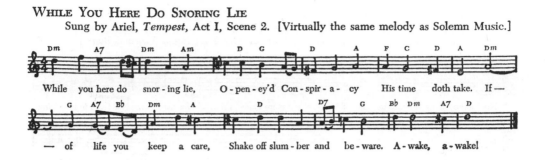

While you here do snor-ing lie, O-pen-ey'd Con-spir-a-cy His time doth take. If—

— of life you keep a care, Shake off slum-ber and be-ware. A-wake, a-wake!

I Shall No More to Sea

Song fragment sung by Stephano, *Tempest*, Act I, Scene 3.

I shall no more to sea, to sea; Here shall I die a - shore.

The Master, the Swabber, the Boatswain, and I

Sung by Stephano, *Tempest*, Act I, Scene 3. [Freely adapted from the traditional tune "Tatter the Road," of which the exact period, source, and provenance are not determinable.]

The mas-ter, the swab-ber, the boat-swain, and I, The gun-ner and his mate Lov'd

Moll, Meg, and Mar-i-an, and Mar-ger-y, But none of us car'd for Kate. For —

she had a tongue with a tang, Would cry to a sail-or, "Go hang!" She lov'd not the sa-vor of

tar nor of pitch, Yet a tail-or might scratch her wher-e'er she did itch. Then — to

sea, boys, and let her go hang! She lov'd not the sa-vor of tar nor of pitch, Yet a

tail-or might scratch her wher-e'er she did itch. Then — to sea, boys, and let her go hang!

No More Dams I'll Make for Fish

Sung by Caliban, *Tempest*, Act I, Scene 3. [Traditional tune "Bony Robin," with refrain adapted from an anonymous "Toye"; both in *The Fitzwilliam Virginal Book*.]

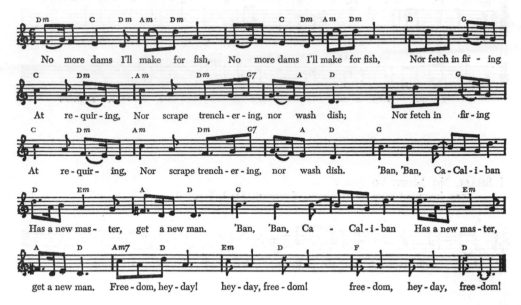

The Catch: Flout 'em and Scout 'em

Trio for Stephano, Trinculo, and Caliban, *Tempest*, Act II, Scene 2. [Adapted from an anonymous "Corranto" in *The Fitzwilliam Virginal Book*.]

'em and scout 'em, scout 'em and flout 'em, Flout 'em and scout 'em; Thought — is free.

Flout 'em and scout 'em, and scout 'em and flout 'em, And flout 'em and scout 'em; Thought — is free.

Flout 'em and scout 'em, and scout 'em and flout 'em, And flout 'em and scout 'em; Thought is free.

FLOUT 'EM AND SCOUT 'EM: THE WRONG TUNE

Duet for Stephano and Trinculo, *Tempest,* Act II, Scene 2.

Stephano

Flout 'em and scout 'em; Thought is free. Flout 'em and scout 'em; Thought is free.

Trinculo

Flout 'em and scout 'em; Thought is free.

THE TUNE OF OUR CATCH

Played by Ariel, on pipe and tabor, *Tempest,* Act II, Scene 2. The Catch, arranged for piano, with small drum if available. Recorders and drum would be suitable for this piece as being the best approximation to the Elizabethan pipe and tabor.

small drum, no snares

SOLEMN AND STRANGE MUSIC

For entrance of the spirits with the banquet, *Tempest*, Act II, Scene 3. [Condensed from a "Galliardo" by Peter Philips in *The Fitzwilliam Virginal Book*.]

A NOISE OF HUNTERS

For entrance of the spirits as dogs, *Tempest*, Act II, Scene 4. This and other horn calls may be played on horn, if available, instead of piano. [Freely adapted from horn call "The Recheat: When the hounds hunt a right game," in Turbeville, *The Noble Art of Venerie* (1575), as interpreted in "Tantivy" by Eric Halfpenny, *Proc. Royal Musical Assoc.*, 80 (1954).]

WHERE THE BEE SUCKS

Sung by Ariel, *Tempest*, Act II, Scene 4. [Composed by Robert Johnson, probably for the first performance of this play in 1611; known to have been used in 1613.]

Where the bee sucks, there suck I ——; In a cow-slip's bell I lie; There I couch where

owls do cry; On the bat's back I do fly Aft-er sum-mer mer-ri-ly.

Mer-ri-ly, mer-ri-ly shall I live now Un-der the blos-som that hangs on the bough.

Mer-ri-ly, mer-ri-ly shall I live now Un-der the blos-som that hangs on the bough.

You Spotted Snakes

Sung by the fairies in *A Midsummer Night's Dream*, Scene 2. Appropriate also as instrumental Entr'acte between Scenes 1 and 2. [Set to the traditional tune "The Leather Bottle" in *Wit and Drollery* (1682). Chappell in *Old English Popular Music* says it is probably much earlier.]

You spot-ted snakes with dou-ble tongue, Thorn-y hedge-hogs
Weav-ing spi-ders, come not here; Hence, you long-legg'd

be not seen, Newts and blind-worms do no wrong,
spin-ners, hence. Bee-tles black, ap-proach not near;

Come not near our Fair-y Queen. Phil-o-mel, with
Worm nor snail, do no of-fense.

mel-o-dy, Sing in our sweet lul-la-by,

Lul-la, lul-la, lul-la-by, lul-la, lul-la,

lul-la-by; Nev-er harm, nor spell, nor charm,

Come our love-ly la-dy nigh. So good night, with

lul-la-by, lul-la, lul-la, Lul-la-by.

The Woosel Cock

Sung by Bottom, *Midsummer Night's Dream*, Scene 2. [Melody long associated with this song. Given by Caulfield in *The Vocal Music in Shakespeare's Plays* (1864?), who unfortunately does not cite a source.]

The woo-sel cock, so black of hue, With or-ange-taw-ny bill, The thros-tle,

with his note so true, The wren, with lit-tle quill, The finch, the spar-row,

and the lark, The plain-song cuck-oo gray, Whose note full man-y a

man doth mark, And dares not an-swer, nay.

221

Horn Call for a Keeper in Parke, Chase, or Forest

To herald entrance of Theseus and Hippolyta, *Midsummer Night's Dream*, Scene 2. [In Turbeville, *The Noble Art of Venerie*.]

Horn Call for the Companie in the Morning

To wake the lovers, *Midsummer Night's Dream*, Scene 2. [In Turbeville, *The Noble Art of Venerie*.]

Flourish: Entrance of Clowns

For entrance of the clowns, *Midsummer Night's Dream*, Scene 3. [Fragment from a "Medley" by William Byrd in *The Fitzwilliam Virginal Book*.]

Bergomask

The clowns' dance, *Midsummer Night's Dream*, Scene 3. [Adapted from a version of the traditional dance tune "La Bergamasca" in Tielman Susato, *Danserye* (1551).]

ROSES, THEIR SHARP SPINES BEING GONE

Sung by the fairies, *Midsummer Night's Dream*, Scene 3. Appropriate also for the fairies' dance at end of Scene 2. [Adapted from the traditional tune "The Leaves Be Greene" in *The Fitzwilliam Virginal Book*.]

FLOURISH

Appropriate in many places: for entrances of the Duke in *Comedy of Errors;* to proclaim Malcolm king, *Macbeth,* Act III, Scene 2; with offer of the crown to Caesar, *Julius Caesar,* Act I, Scene 1. [Adapted from a variation of "Pescodd Time" by William Byrd in *The Fitzwilliam Virginal Book.*]

ALARUM A

With entrance of Duncan, meeting a bleeding captain, in *Macbeth,* Act I, Scene 1. Also for the battles in *Macbeth,* Act III, Scene 2, and in *Julius Caesar,* Act II, Scene 2. [English military signal "Charge!" Portion of suite "The Battell" by William Byrd in *My Ladye Nevells Booke* (1591).]

DRUM MARCH

For entrances of Macbeth, and his army, *Macbeth,* Act I, Scene 1, and Act III, Scene 2. Appropriate also for entrances of armies of Brutus and Cassius, *Julius Caesar,* Act II, Scenes 1 and 2. May be played by piano alone, by drums alone, or by both. ["Marche of Footemen" in Byrd's Battell suite.]

SENNET

For *Macbeth:* entrance of King Duncan, Act I, Scene 2; entrance of Macbeth as King, Act II, Scene 1; and the show of eight kings in the witches' cavern, Act II, Scene 2. Appropriate also for Caesar's entrances and exits, *Julius Caesar*, Act I, Scene 1; if a longer piece is wanted here, use "The Earle of Oxford's March." This sennet suitable for oboes with wind band, or for brass. [From Byrd's "Medley."]

MUSIC FOR HOBOYES

For the banquets in *Macbeth:* Act I, Scene 2 (offstage); Act II, Scene 1 (on stage). [From a "Medley" by Edward Johnson in *The Fitzwilliam Virginal book.*]

TRUMPET AND DRUM MARCH

For entrances of Malcolm and his army, *Macbeth,* Act III, Scene 2. Appropriate also for entrance of Antony and Octavius (and army), *Julius Caesar,* Act II, Scene 2. May be played by piano alone, by drums alone, by piano and drums, or by trumpet and drums. [Portion of "The Trumpetts," from Byrd's Battell suite.]

ALARUM B

For the battles in *Macbeth,* Act III, Scene 2, and in *Julius Caesar,* Act II, Scene 2.
[Adapted from portions of a vocal number "La Bataille" by Clément Janequin (1529).
The signals identified are: "Mount horses," "Rally 'round the flag," and "Forward."]

FORTUNE, MY FOE

Song appropriate for Lucius to sing to Brutus, *Julius Caesar*, Act II, Scene 1. [One of the best-known traditional songs of Shakespeare's day. Shakespeare mentions it in two plays. Chappell dates it from 1565.]

Fortune, my foe, why dost thou frown on me?
And will thy favor never better be?
Wilt thou, I say, for ever breed me pain,
And wilt thou not restore my joys again?

THE EARLE OF OXFORD'S MARCH

A versatile piece, suitable as Overture for most of the plays. As Overture and Entr'acte (between Scenes 2 and 3) for *Midsummer Night's Dream*, it would add pomp and grandeur to the entrances of Theseus and Hippolyta. Appropriate also for Caesar's entrances (and exits) in *Julius Caesar*, Act I, Scene 1. [Condensed from a virginal piece by William Byrd which appears in *My Ladye Nevells Booke* and in *The Fitzwilliam Virginal Book*.]

Glossary

A — sometimes used for "he"

ABATE — to shorten

ABIDE — to pay the penalty for: "Let no man abide this deed but we the doers."

ABUSE — to deceive

ACCENTS — languages

ADDITION — title, mark of distinction

ADDRESSED — ready: "The Prologue is addressed"

AGAINST — in anticipation of

AGUE — illness, usually with chills and fever

ALARUM — summons to battle by trumpet or drum; also, an attack, or the noise of battle in general

ALCHEMY — the pseudoscience of turning base metals into gold

AMAIN — swiftly, strongly

AN — if, as if

ANGELS — gold coins

ANNOYANCE — injury, harm

ANON — soon

ANSWER — to discharge a debt or fulfill an obligation; also, to return a blow, to retaliate

ANTIC — quaint, grotesque, fantastic; also, ancient, antique

ASSURED — promised; betrothed

ATE — the goddess of mischief and vengeance

ATTACH — to arrest

AUDITOR — a listener

AUGURER — an augur, a member of the highest class of official diviners of ancient Rome

BADGED — marked plainly; the expression comes from the fact that servants wore badges to indicate whom they served

BAND — a bond

BANE — destruction, ruin

BARNACLE — a kind of wild goose, thought to hatch from seashells (barnacle shells) growing on trees by the seashore

BASIS — the base or pedestal of a statue

BATE — to abate or reduce

BATTLE — battalion, troop, or division

BAY — to bark at; also to bring to bay

BEADS — rosary

BEAK — prow of a ship

BEAR OFF — to ward off, to protect from

BELLMAN — watchman, town crier

BEND UP — to make tense or ready for action

BERGOMASK — a peasant dance from Bergamo, Italy

BETIMES — early

BILLS — written orders

BLAZE — to proclaim

BLOOD-BOLTER'D — having the hair matted with blood

BLUNT — stupid; also rude, abrupt

BOND — a promise, a legal agreement

BOTTLE — a bundle

BRAKE — a thicket, underbrush

BRAVE — fine, splendid, admirable

BREAK — to reveal a secret, to make a disclosure

BRINDED — archaic form of brindled, meaning streaked or spotted

BROOK — to bear, endure, or tolerate

BUFF — a kind of leather having a dull whitish-yellow color, used for the clothing of sheriff's officers and soldiers

BURTHEN — burden, a heavy load; also the chorus of a song

BUT — sometimes means "only," as in "But screw your courage to the sticking-place"

BUTT — a large cask or barrel

CANKERBLOSSOM — a worm that destroys a blossom

CARCANET — an ornamental collar or necklace

CARRION — dead and rotting

CASE — condition: "I am in case to justle a constable"

CATCH — a round, in which one singer catches at the words of another; also, to seize

CAVALERY — cavalier or cavalero, meaning gallant gentleman

CENSURE — to judge

CEREMONIES — external accessories or symbolical attributes of worship, state, or pomp

CHANGE — exchange

CHANGELING — fairies were supposed to steal mortal children and leave fairy children in exchange; both those stolen and those left were called changelings

CHAPLET — a wreath or garland for the head

CHARGE — to load or burden

CHARGEFUL — expensive, costly

CHIDE — to quarrel or brawl

CLEAR — pure, innocent

CLING — to shrivel up, to wither

CLOSE — secluded, secret

CLOSET — study, private room

COFFER — treasury

COIL — turmoil, disturbance

COLD — halfhearted

COLOSSUS — gigantic statue of Apollo, said to have stood with one foot on each side of the harbor of Rhodes in ancient times, one of the Seven Wonders of the World

COMPACT — composed of; also, an agreement

CON — to learn or memorize

CONCEIT — imagination, thought; idea, conception

CONCEITED — understood

CONFEDERATE — to conspire or form an alliance with; also, united, allied

CONFOUND — to ruin or destroy; also, to stun with dismay

CONVINCE — to overcome

CORPORAL — corporeal, having a body; bodily, pertaining to the body

CORRESPONDENT — to be submissive

COURSE — the racecourse; also, an inning or round in the sport of bearbaiting

COY — to pat, caress

CROW — a crowbar

CULL OUT — to pick out, to select

CUMBER — to harass, to trouble

DALLIANCE — dallying, wasting time

DAM — female parent, usually applied to lower animals; in *The Tempest* it refers to Caliban's mother

DEAR EXPENSE — "If I have thanks, it is a dear expense": Helena probably means that the thanks she will get will cost her dearly, for she will be helping the one she loves in his effort to win another girl

DECLINE — to incline

DEGREE — rank

DELIVER — to relate, to report

DILATE — to relate in detail

DIRECTLY — straight, to the point

DISCOVERY — reconnaissance

DISMAL — disastrous

DISPATCH — management; as a verb it means to put to death; also, to make haste

DISSEMBLE — to disguise; to conceal

DISTINCTLY — separately, individually

DISTRACT — insane

DIVERS — several; of different kinds

DIVINER — sorcerer, one who foretells

DOIT — an almost worthless coin

DOTAGE — infatuation

DOWL — a fluffy bit of down, a part of a feather

DRACHMA — a Greek silver coin

DUDGEON — handle

EARNEST — a sum paid in advance to seal a bargain

ECSTASY — a fit of madness

EKE — also

ELL — a measure of length, 1¼ yards

ENGAGE — to promise, to pledge

ENSIGN — standard; also the standard-bearer

EQUIVOCATION — deliberate ambiguity, the use of terms susceptible of double meaning in order to deceive

ERCLES — Hercules

EVER — always

EXEUNT — a stage direction in Latin, meaning "they go out"

EXHALATIONS — meteors: "The exhalations whizzing in the air"

EXIT — a stage direction in Latin, meaning "he [or she] goes out"

EXTIRPATE — to drive away or expel

EYNE — eyes

FACTIOUS — active as a partisan; "be factious" means to assemble a faction or party

FANTASTICAL — imaginary

FANTASY — imagination, fancy

FEATLY — nimbly and gracefully

FELL — fierce, cruel, angry

FEN — a marsh or bog

FILED — defiled

FIRSTLING — firstborn

FLEERING — sneering, grinning contemptuously

FLOURISH — a trumpet fanfare

FOND — foolish, doting

FORDONE — overdone, exhausted

FORK — forked tongue

FORMAL — in proper form, regular; rational, sane

FORTH — out, away from home

FRAME — to invent, to shape, to make

FRANTIC — mad, insane

FRAUGHTAGE — cargo, freight

FRET — to checker or variegate

FRIPPERY — an old clothes shop

GABARDINE — a cloak

GENERAL — the general body of the people, the public, the multitude

GENIUS — attendant spirit, personification

GET — to beget, to father

GLASS — hourglass ("two glasses" means two o'clock); also, mirror; in *Macbeth* the word refers to a magic mirror or crystal ball in which the future can be seen

GORGON — a mythical monster, which turned the beholder to stone

GOSSIP — a baptismal sponsor; applied more generally, the term includes all those invited to a christening, as well as the merrymaking itself

GOUT — clot, thick drop

GROW — to accrue, to fall due

GULF — gullet

HALBERDS — long-handled battle-axes

HARP — to guess

HARPIER — the name of a demon, the Third Witch's attendant spirit (probably a corruption of Harpy)

HATCH — a half-door; "sit down at the hatch" refers to the proverb "to set a hatch before the door," meaning to keep silent

HAVING — possession: "prediction of noble having and of royal hope"

HAVOC — in medieval warfare, the order or command for pillaging and slaughter

HAZARD — risk; "on the hazard" means at stake

HECATE — a triple goddess in Greek mythology: on earth she was Diana, in the heavens she was Phoebe the moon goddess, and in the underworld she was Hecate, goddess of witchcraft and magic

HEMPEN HOMESPUNS — those who are dressed in garments of homespun cloth made of hemp, which was very rough and coarse, rather like burlap

HIEMS — winter personified

HIGHT — is called

HOBOYES — hautboys, oboes; this spelling indicates Shakespeare's pronunciation of the French *hautbois,* of which the English word "oboe" is a corruption

HOODWINK — to blindfold (from a hawking term meaning to put a hood over the hawk's head); "hoodwink this mischance" means to blind one to this misfortune

HOST — to lodge at an inn; the innkeeper

HOWLET — an owlet

HUMBLE-BEE — a bumblebee

IDES OF MARCH — March 15

IDLY — madly, absurdly

IMBRUE — to stain with blood

IMPEACH — an accusation

INCARNADINE — to redden

INCHMEAL — inch by inch, piecemeal

INDIRECTION — malpractice, dishonesty

INJURY — an insult or affront

INSANE ROOT — a root producing insanity

INSTANCE — indication, proof, evidence

INTERMIT — to delay, or to prevent

JACK — knave or rascal (the Jack in a deck of cards is called the knave)

JUMP — to risk

JUSTIFY — to prove

JUSTLE — to jostle, to elbow or push

KIND — nature; also, "in this kind" means "in this respect"

KNAVE — boy, youth; frequently applied to servants with friendly familiarity

KNOT — company, group

LAKIN — ladykin, an affectionate term for the Virgin Mary; "by'r lakin" is a mild oath meaning "by our ladykin"

LATCH — to catch; also, to bind with a spell

LIVERY — any distinguishing dress, a uniform

LOB — a bumpkin

LONG OF — on account of, because of

LOON — lout, rascal; man of low rank

LOVE-IN-IDLENESS — the pansy

LOVE-SPRINGS — first tender buds of love

LUGGAGE — encumbrance

MAKE HEAD — to raise an army

MALT-HORSE — a clumsy kind of cart horse used by brewers

MARRY — an interjection or mild oath from the name of the Virgin Mary

MATED — dazed, amazed, confounded

MAW — stomach

MAZED — amazed, astonished, bewildered

MEANER — of lower class

MEANLY — moderately

MEASURE — proportion

MECHANICALS — workingmen

MEET — fitting, proper

METTLE — the stuff of which man is made, hence courage

MICKLE — much

MINION — darling, favorite

MINISTERS — agents

MISPRISED — mistaken, misunderstood

MISSIVES — messengers

MOE — more

MOME — blockhead, dolt, simpleton

MONSTROUS — abnormal, contrary to nature

MOONCALF — a malformed animal, a monstrosity, thought to be caused by the action of the moon

MUMMY — a powder made from mummified flesh and used as a drug

NAPKINS — handkerchiefs

NIGHTGOWN — dressing gown

NOLL — a jocular or contemptuous term for head

NOR . . . NOR — neither . . . nor

OBSCURE BIRD — the owl, bird of darkness and of ill omen

O'ER-RAUGHT — cheated

O'ERWATCHED — tired out by being kept awake

OFFICES — duties

OLD — a colloquial term meaning plenty of

OMIT — to miss or to neglect

OR . . . OR — either . . . or

ORCHARD — garden

ORDINANCE — natural behavior as decreed by God

OUT — quite, fully: "Thou wast not out three years old"

OWE — to own or have

PACKED WITH — in league with

PALE — fence

PALTER — to equivocate, to trick

PAP — breast

PARCEL — a part

PASSING — exceedingly

PATCH — a fool (derived from the fool's multicolored costume)

PEASCOD — a peapod

PERDIE — a corruption of *par Dieu*, a trivial oath meaning "by God"

PHIBBUS — Phoebus Apollo, the sun god

PHILOMEL — classical name for the nightingale

PIPE AND TABOR — small flute and small drum, both played by a single musician; the pipe was held and played by the left hand, leaving the right hand free for beating the tabor, which hung from the player's neck, waist, or left arm

PITCH — a term from falconry, meaning the height to which a falcon soars

PLAINSONG — ecclesiastical chants in a minor key with simple and unvarying melody, hence the use of the term for the cuckoo's monotonous song in a minor third

PLUMMET — a sounding lead, a heavy weight attached to the end of a line, for measuring depth

POINT — in "performed to point": performed in every point, exactly

PORTENT — an omen or sign, a forewarning

PORTENTOUS — of the nature of a portent

POSTER — one who rides swiftly or posthaste

POWER — sometimes means army or armed forces

PREMISES — conditions, stipulations

PRESENT — immediate

PRESENTLY — at once, immediately

PRICK — to incite or spur; also, to mark with a check

PRODIGIOUS — threatening, ominous

PRODIGY — something extraordinary, out of the usual course of nature, hence an omen

PROPER — one's own, personal

PUISSANCE — power, strength; armed forces

PUISSANT — powerful, mighty

PULL IN — to rein in

QUAIL — to overpower, to intimidate

QUELL — to destroy, to kill

QUICK — lively

QUILL — a hollow cane used as a musical pipe, the smaller the pipe the higher the pitch

RACK — a floating cloud or mist

RAPT — lost in revery

RAVELED — tangled

RAVINED — ravenous

RECEIVE — to understand, to accept as true

RECORDER — a flute-like wind instrument

RECOVER — to cause to recover, to revive; also, to get or obtain

REEDS, EAVES OF — a thatched roof

REMEMBER — sometimes means to cause to remember, or to remind

REMEMBRANCER — one who reminds another

RENDER — to surrender

REPEAL — recall (from exile)

REQUIT — past participle of requite, meaning to repay

REREMICE — bats

RESOLUTION — freedom from doubt

RESOLVE — to make certain

RESTING — immovable, stable

RIVE — to split

ROAD — roadstead, harbor

ROARERS — huge waves or billows

ROUGH-CAST — plaster mixed with pebbles

ROUND — crown; also, a round dance or roundel

ROUNDEL — a country dance in which the dancers form a circle

RUBS — roughness, unevenness

RUDE — uncivilized, uncultured

SACK — sherry (wine)

SAD — serious, grave

SANS FABLE — without falsehood

SCAPE — to escape

SCHEDULE — a written scroll

SEAT — a situation or site; also, to settle

SEEL — a term from falconry, meaning to blind by sewing the eyelids together

SELF — one's own; same

SENNET — a trumpet signal

SENSELESS — incapable of feeling

SENSIBLE — sensitive, capable of feeling

SERE — withered

SEVERAL — individual

SHADOW — a spirit, something insubstantial, bodiless; also, to shade or partially to conceal

SIEGE — excrement

SISTERS THREE — the three Fates

SLEAVE — a fine filament of silk obtained by separating a thicker thread

SLIP — "let slip" means to unleash

SMATCH — a smack, or flavor

SOFT — stop, wait a moment

SOLEMN — official, formal, ceremonial

SORT — to turn out or to result; also, to be appropriate to or befit

SOT — fool, idiot

SOUND — to measure depth; to dive suddenly straight down; to probe, or try to find the thoughts of another

SPECULATION — sight, power of seeing

SPORT — amusement

SPOTTED — stained morally

SPRING — earliest part, beginning; first tender shoot or bud of a plant

SPURN — to kick

SQUASH — the unripe pod of a pea

STALE — a decoy

STAND UPON — to concern; to be particular about

STARE — to stand on end

STAY — to wait; to await; also, to cause to stay, or prevent from going

STEADED — assisted, helped, stood in good stead

STILL — always, ever, constantly

STOMACH — courage; inclination, disposition

STRANGE — unaccustomed, extraordinary; also, to be astonished, as at something new and strange

SUBORN — by underhand means to induce someone to commit an unworthy deed

SUBTILTY — illusion; also, an artful plan

SURCEASE — discontinuance; death

SURGES — billows, waves

SURVEY — to perceive or notice

SUSTAINING GARMENTS — buoyant clothing which, like water wings, keep the wearer afloat

SWAY — dominion

TABOR — small drum; see "pipe and tabor"

TAINT — to be infected

TAKE OFF — to kill or destroy

TAPER — candle

TESTY — headstrong; petulant

THORNBUSH — English peasants saw the man in the moon as bearing a bundle of sticks on his back; an old tale went that the man was banished to the moon with his dog for gathering brush on Sunday

THREEFOLD WORLD — the Roman empire: Europe, Asia, and Africa

THROUGHLY — thoroughly

THRUM — a term from weaving, meaning the loose ends of the lengthwise threads (the warp); "cut thread and thrum" means to cut everything

'TIDE — to betide, to come

TIRING HOUSE — the dressing room in a theater

TOWARD — in preparation

TRAMMEL UP — to hold or entangle, as in a kind of fishnet called a trammel

TRENCHERING — trenchers, or wooden plates

TRIUMPH — splendid show or festival

TROTH — truth, faith

TRUMPERY — something deceptively showy; worthless trash

UNBEND — to relax, to slacken

UP-STARING — standing on end

USE — the natural order of things, normality

UTTERMOST — latest

VAIN — false; extravagant; silly

VANTAGE — advantage, opportunity

VAWARD — vanward, forepart, early part

VENTURES — anything hazarded or risked on an enterprise

VOTARESS — a woman consecrated by a vow

VULGAR — the common people; also, common or public

WAFT — to beckon; also, to transport by sea

WAFTAGE — passage by boat, transportation

WAIST — midship

WANTING — lacking

WARN — to defy or challenge

WARRANT — justification

WATCH — the night watch, night patrol

WEEDS — garments

WELL-ADVISED — in one's right mind

WEZAND — windpipe

WHILE — until

WHILERE — a while ago

WHIST — hushed, silent, quiet

WIND — to blow: "Horns winded within" means horns are blown offstage

WINK — to shut the eyes; also, to sleep; "the perpetual wink" means death

WITHIN — a stage direction meaning offstage

WONT — ordinary manner of doing or acting, habit

WONTED — customary, usual

WOOSEL COCK — ousel cock, male blackbird

WOT — to know

WRACK — old form of wreck; also means ruin

YARE — ready; also, quick or brisk

YARELY — nimbly, quickly